Compositions and Concepts

Compositions and Concepts

Carei F. Thomas

CAJOLE PRODUCTIONS
MINNEAPOLIS

Published by:
Cajole Productions
Carei F. Thomas
P.O. Box 7081
Minneapolis, MN 55407-7081

Book design by Dorie McClelland, Spring Book Design
Front cover photo by James Taylor
Back cover photo by Paulette Myers-Rich
Cover graphic by Carei F. Thomas

Printed in the United States of America.
First printing.
First edition.

ISBN: 978-0-615-36180-2

Contents

Acknowledgments

I would like to extend a very special thank you to my family, friends, mentors, teachers, neighbors and places that so enriched my life. Some of these include:

Frank N. and Mary M.A. Thomas, Rebecca Boyd, William C. Boyd, The Gohonzon, SGI-USA, Carol LaPierre Thomas, my children Joi, Jaahred and Aairam and their families, Joyce M. Thomas, Eleanora Lesesne, Manfred Sales, Melvin Peterson, Gregory "Duke" Hall, Pat Parker, Donald "Rafael" Garrett, Kalaparusha Maurice McIntyre, John Blanton, Antoinette Williams, The Center, Douglas Ewart, Janis-Lane Ewart, Karen Starr, James Bransford, Gary Schulte, Steve Kimmel, The Rainbow Gallery, Reginald Buckner, Todd Harper, T.J. Anderson, Alvin Singleton, David Murray, James Newton, Joe Smith, Homer Lambrecht, Milo Fine, Warren Park, Donald and Faye Washington, Jeffrey Brooks, Anthony Cox, David Wright, John and Joan Minczeski, Zeitgeist, Louis Alemayehu, Mick LaBriola, Steven Linsner, Emma Slaughter, Leigh Kamman, Mary Roark, Tom Surowicz, Bob Protzman, Steven Rueff, and on and on and on.

I am also appreciative of the schools and organizations in the Twin Cities who have recognized my work through awards, residencies and board memberships, and to Dorie McClelland of Spring Book Design who worked so diligently with me on putting this book together.

And, for all those people who are not listed here and have contributed to my development, YOU KNOW WHO YOU ARE! I am grateful. Thank you.

The Journey and the Destination are the Same!

DEPOT

Light is seldom discerned
alone as a friend of darkness
Yet out of humility bursts this target of
reality, lost, but none the less,
defined . . . complex but complete
This brief reality—this life's moment
Everspinning . . . spinning . . . spinning and
spinning like an eternal HYMN
. . . NO REFERENCES NECESSARY
NO LIGHT . . .
. . . NO DARKNESS

Carei F. Thomas
October, 1992

CAREI THOMAS

Carey Frank Thomas is the son of Frank Nebraska Thomas and Mary Majesta Anderson Thomas. He has a daughter (Joi), two sons (Jaahred and Aairam), and seven grandchildren (Noah, Avery, Myles, Chloe, Malik, Ava and Aaidan). His career got its start in Pittsburgh, Pennsylvania, where he took piano lessons and was influenced by the culturally diverse Hill District. During his musical career, he changed the spelling of his name to Carei.

Carei's family moved to Chicago during his teenage years. While in high school, he formed a doo-wop group and continued expanding his artistry through an interest in spontaneous vocal composition. In 1959, Carei enrolled in Chicago's Roosevelt University. Also that year, he chanced-met Gregory "Duke" Hall who was staying on Chicago's West Side where Carei lived. This was a pivotal time in his development. "Duke" introduced him to elemental jazz piano voicings and four-part modern vocal harmony as used by the Hi Lo's and Four Freshmen. Carei was in the U.S. Army from 1961 to 1963 in Germany and, when he returned, he enrolled in the Chicago Musical College.

In the late 1960s, Carei sat in on piano with Dexter Gordon and Art Taylor in Paris, debuted his first significant jazz ensemble at Dunbar High School, of which Ari Brown of the Ethnic Heritage Ensemble fame was a part, began an alliance with members of the internationally-known Association for the Advancement of Creative Musicians (AACM), sat in with Archie Shepp at Mother Blues on Wells Street in "Old Town" Chicago, co-founded (with Kalaparusha Maurice McIntyre) a group called "The Light," and gigged at Alice's Restaurant on Chicago's North Side with Marion Brown. During this time, Carei continued playing piano as a means to realize or hear "outside" the compositions going on "inside" his head . . . soul . . . self.

In 1972, Carei moved to Minneapolis and briefly studied composition at the University of Minnesota. He then began developing several controlled improvisational concepts he called "Brief Realities," all of which exemplified how he wanted to utilize composition in fresh ways (ever going back and forth chronologically in pendulum fashion) uniting that which was with the ever-present possibilities of "now time." He also started doing residencies in educational settings due to the encouragement of mentor Reginald Buckner.

In the 1980s, Carei worked on other evolutions of controlled improvisations, became interested in the healing aspects of sound and color and in having his artform be more than a performer/spectator one with "down to earth" functionality. In the 1990s, Carei added to his work the "smoke and mirrors" of acoustical and electronic music considerations, which he called Phononomalies. He liked developing these tonal fabrics (sound designs) to use them as a canvas accommodating the collaborative endeavors of poetry, spoken work, dance, video, visual artforms, theatre, etc., along with their closest friend . . . Silence.

In 1993, Carei became seriously ill with Guillain-Barré Syndrome and was hospitalized and in physical rehabilitation until 1995. However, he continued to create and has adapted his hands to produce chords much like the ones he played before he was paralyzed.

Carei's work in the Twin Cities has been recognized through awards and commissions and he has held residencies from kindergarten through college. He has founded and co-founded musical ensembles playing diverse works and has produced a variety of interdisciplinary events for the community.

Reviews and Quotes

(Used with permission)

Tom Surowicz in a *Twin Cities Reader* article said,
"Thomas' music is playful, harmonious, energetic, dynamic, buoyant, and one-of-a-kind. It's more life-affirming than a bushel of stuffy string quartets, or a Sahara of dry computer compositions. Thomas' work is indeed macro, beaming out in a multitude of directions." And, Mr. Surowicz in another *Reader* article said, "Carei Thomas' fanciful original jazz is one of the most joyous noises the Twin Cities musical community has to offer."

Dr. Carleton Macy, Music Chair at Macalester College, said the following about Carei's work:
"Thomas' compositions are unusual and multi-faceted; they encompass an historic range of musical styles, expressing social and personal experiences and observations. Carei brings with him an infectious sense of community and unity of purpose which is likewise communicated in his music."

"[Thomas'] user-friendly compositions lighten the theoretical rigor of avant-jazz with playful humor and friendly tunefulness."

—Cecile Cloutier, *City Pages*

"It seems that every few years, some unknown treasure of American improvised music pops up after decades of toil in relative obscurity . . . this is fine, passionate music . . . a pleasant surprise, and [it] will surely please listeners as it did me."

—Jason Bivins, *Cadence*

"Carei Thomas' music is a beautiful challenge. I've played his music for 21 years. His music reflects yesterday, today and the future."

—Donald Washington, Musician/Educator

"Carei F. Thomas is one of the rare composers whose music possesses highly personal contemporary techniques, yet, never loses contact with humanity. I have followed his multidisciplinary approach since 1991 and continue to be impressed with his ability to link his music and personal intensity with community spirit."

—T.J. Anderson, Professor of Music Emeritus at Tufts University

"Among the many facets to Carei Thomas are philosopher, visionary, artist, improviser of spoken word, theoretician, pianist, singer. He's an alchemist of synesthesia and synchronicity in which a simple fragrance can transform into colors, emotions, images. The amazing thing about Carei is his ability to translate these things into music. They are remarkable and expansive compositions, which he has taught to the many musicians who have played with him over the past half-century. Now, with this book of his collected works, this important music is finally accessible to everyone."

—John Minczeski, Poet

"Carei Thomas is one of America's most original and eclectic composition voices writing today. Long loved and recognized, his work for many years has been emanating from the heart of the American Midwest . . . Thomas' music is arresting, memorable and profound, all matched by the zeal of his artistic personality and humanity."

—Dr. Bill Banfield, Composer

Foreword

Gary Schulte

Carei Thomas is our neighborhood's friendly genius. I want you to understand, perform and love his music, as collected in this book, because I know it to be truly unique in its uncompromising breadth of style and vision. Coming as he does out of the Black cultural tradition of improvisation and performance composition, this task of understanding can sometimes be a slippery one, for these compositions are process rather than product oriented. Furthermore, the music and the man are inseparable. Because he cannot stand still and will not be pinned down or see anything as static, I can sometimes think that the irrepressibly creative, stubbornly single-minded, constantly shifting and evolving pianist-composer Carei Thomas has sometimes unwittingly distracted us from seeing some of his tunes and studies as the MASTERPIECES that they truly are. We love Carei for the rich community he has made of us and all the gifts he has fostered in us as he invited us into his neighborhood of ensembles and collaborative work and into his pieces and has allowed us to help him make them come alive. But now is the time for the works themselves to be seen and honored on their own merits. And it is our task to keep playing and exploring them, whether Carei is around or not.

Here we present you with an astonishing collection of Carei's work, a book bursting at the seams with it, the work of a lifetime. What are we to make of all this? Lest you be immediately confused, let me prepare you a little. You are about to encounter Carei's compositional chart. Most of us in the Western tradition are used to reading from the top down, but this chart reads bottoms up. Actually, you read it BOTH WAYS, Carei says, and that makes sense. A tree grows from the ground up. We journey out from the source and can at any time journey back, as we often do when playing Carei's compositions via improvisation. In playing his material, we often spontaneously compose, using his tunes and tone rows as points of departure, and as quotes along the way.

To understand Carei's music, you must first understand him. Consider his childhood in Pittsburgh's famous Hill District of the 1940s, the venerable old brownstones rising up and down steep inclines, the neighborhood filled with characters of all kinds that have peopled his compositions and informed their venerable, anthem-like, bizarre, jocular, cartoonic, at times theatrical and programmatic character. There were immigrants around him from all cultures the world over, and he credits this background with the creation of his ecumenical, pan-cultural view that is so important for us to comprehend as a guide to the playing of his work.

Imagine a small boy seated at a piano in a grand old house. He is oblivious to everything except his treasure trove, the music he is searching for and that is finding him. And he is doing this in a very special way. He is improvising, which I think is the greatest gift to us all from his Black cultural tradition. You don't hear him noodling his way over chords or merely developing a theme. He is having a musical conversation with everything around him. This improvisation, even by this small and gifted boy, is actual composition in the moment of playing and performance. The piano and Carei, and the house in its stillness, are suddenly one. His soft, beautiful doe eyes seem to mist over as he plays in dialog with the sirens out there on the street and the voices of all the eccentric neighborhood characters, or the laughter or clatter or sharp words of the women in the house.

Carei was a product of an only child's solitude and reflection, coupled with a rich community life. He grew up in a protected, nurturing atmosphere of culture and sensitivity, his mother playing violin and string bass, his aunt a powerful and highly literate orator. He was no weakling or hermit. He stole watermelons and did other things boys will do. At the same time, he was developing a wide range of appreciation, from his own piano playing to the sounds of other instruments, from jazz to the most modern and sophisticated Scriabinesque or Bartok-ian classical voyages and forms, and to the most abstract of visual art, dance, performance art, poetry-music dialog, the collaborative process and world. In his teens his family moved to Chicago and he became part of the cultural scene that produced the Art Ensemble of Chicago, and developed his composer-performer aspects and collaborative ones and the out-there improvisations and the insistence on breaking the mold of any one kind or style of music. Then he moved to Minneapolis to attend the University of Minnesota and study composition and music therapy, as he was already interested in the healing arts as well. To this day, any visit to his home causes you to come away filled with the energy and inspiration to create, in any form.

A dream period of my life, and one of my fondest memories, is of Carei and I collaborating regularly as a violin-piano duo, playing and improvising on his so-called SIMPLE SONGS, back in the early to mid-1980s. I can't tell you what wonder I felt as I stepped into this new world of Carei's music, so approachable and challenging at the same time, so lyrical and of a healing spirit, and so richly programmatic, taking you so many places and embracing so many styles and personalities. I know these tunes to be masterpieces every bit in league with Ellington's songs or the melodies of the European classicists, and at the same time they stand on their own. As Bartok called the songs of his own culture MASTERPIECES IN MINIATURE, so it is with these strangely beautiful melodies, and the unique polytonal harmonies underpinning them.

Carei penned these compositions with chords like jazz charts in his neat and artistic hand. I still possess and treasure soft and much fingered originals of some of these tunes. They are deceptively simple. Because of their complexity and sophistication, a jazz chart simply cannot convey or hold them. Soon you realize that these often gentle and innocent sounding melodies take surprising twists and turns. In the past, when musicians played these charts in traditional jazz contexts they would be baffled by some of the chord symbols he wrote. Indeed, some players did mistake the correct tonal center when playing over them. Even though some of Carei's chords go to the limit of tonality, they still have a distinct tonal center in relation to the melody, and because they are polytonal it is easy to lose touch with this.

As you look over these charts and compositions, listen to recordings of Carei playing the chords to these songs. Pay particular attention to songs such as TURN LEFT, YOU CAN'T MISS IT about Carei's pilgrimage trying to find Charlie Parker's grave, and HOME CLEAN about his experience in recovery. These are among the masterpieces of his style. Recordings pre-fall of 1993, before his illness, of groups such as the TRIADE piano trio show him playing material such as this, and recordings, if available, of Carei and I doing our duo work, or Carei with Eddie Berger. Listen to the mind-blowing voicings of the chords, the polytonality, so beautiful but at times dissonant like hoarfrost on the windowsill. Analyze them, orchestrate them, blow over them, carry them on.

Carei's music manifests a challenging personality and essence that sometimes people don't get when he's not in the room or not playing himself. While Carei was ill and unable to participate in the directing and playing of his music, sometimes folks didn't get those harmonies or the spirit behind the work and only focussed on the free aspect. But fortunately, when Carei had his 70th birthday celebration, all the musicians who came out to perform for him at Walker Art Center got the music just fine, and the session later at the Dakota jazz club showed musicians truly playing it in its harmonic structure and spirit. I hope musicians and listeners will continue to make the effort to understand and learn from Carei's work because I think it echoes the qualities of a bygone and better time—an earthy multicultural neighborhood of character, innocence, kindness, gentleness, purity, lyricism, playfulness, frankness and yet a joy of life even amid its hardships.

Here is the work of a vivid, active, multidisciplinary and unconventionally creative mind. Just when you're rhapsodizingly enfolded in the dream of his melodies, he casts the fly in the ointment and hits you with one of his tone rows. Almost like a pedantic teacher hanging over you, he makes you read pitches as letters rather than notes on the staff, and with numbers over them telling you how long to hold the notes. You have to adjust and shift your mode of thinking totally. But that's Carei, always catching you off guard, sending you in a new direction. As you can see from the chart, the simple songs are the foundation but only a small part of Carei's work as it has evolved over the decades. He might hit you with HELIX, his brilliant fugal study, played as a fugue but then developed via improvisation. Or it might be his BAMIDJIAN SCAAAL, or a still life or montage. You'll see note and sound studies, and textural studies, and compositions organized not only along normal musical lines but along the lines of visual art or even fragrances.

To apprehend Carei's music, it helps to understand the performance context. Imagine him calling you to play on one of his concert gigs. In this way he will challenge you not only with the music itself but with the groups of musicians you will play with. Here you may find odd and sometimes provoking, sometimes playful assortments of instruments and personalities he has chosen that you have to interface with in true dialog, true meeting and melding, however awkward or sublime and spiritual. Sometimes when you and the others play those tone rows or scores he's so carefully crafted, he nevertheless wants you all to be a little sloppy with them, let them spill over at the edges. A concert title of his describes this perfectly: A GIFT OF PAGES BENT. He might even invite a poet or improvisational dancer or performance painter to be part of the collaboration. This puts an even greater burden of responsibility on you to truly listen and respond. When you check out recordings of ANCESTOR ENERGY or MOTHERCHILD poetry-jazz, pay particular attention to how Carei moves way beyond the usual riffs or grooves that often merely accompany performance poets. Instead, Carei's music truly converses with them. In this book you will find anthems and songs, transcendent musical motifs that show a very different approach to spoken word for the improvising musician—tuneful, respectful, thankful, reaching for the dawn.

Despite how earthy or jazzy or way out Carei's restless performance extravaganzas have been, he has often had a strong thread of chamber music and the classical running through them. Back in the mid-1980s, just when I thought I had Carei all to myself in our duo collaboration, he invited at the last minute a cellist to join us in a concert, and TRIADE improvisational piano trio was born. By this time I was very familiar with Carei's tunes and harmonies and we were playing them in a seamless spontaneous compositional style. This led to the first performance of what Carei calls BRIEF REALITIES, a concept that baffled even myself when I first heard him describe it in one of our interviews on Minnesota Public Radio. What we were actually doing was creating lyrical, well ordered composition spontaneously in the flow of performance, and we knew the tunes and material so well and had developed it over so long a time that we were creating a compositional fabric sometimes entirely separate from the tunes, which we'd go back to and quote on occasion. Here was a wonderful musical free association and the recordings of our first collaboration at Toad Hall performance space, and subsequent ones at Walker Church and Janet Wallace recital hall at Macalester College, bear witness to this. I hope folks will listen carefully to this work and apprehend that it is not jazz alone but a continuum of style, that it is a classical chamber music composed of strong and distinct elements from the Western European tradition, but in a completely improvised way, and that it is possible for a group of instrumentalists TOGETHER to create this kind of seamless work that is completely improvised and yet very carefully composed in the moment of performance.

After Carei's illness, when he made his triumphant comeback, he did a lot more work on synthesizer and electronics, which he calls PHONONOMALY, and also in sophisticated written composition. With the computer tools that were becoming available he began creating scores with different instruments assigned to parts, which he had done to a more limited extent before. This brought a whole new dimension and texture to Carei's style. Recordings from this period include performances of the re-formed TRIADE at Intermedia Arts, and the SOUND WINDOWS ensemble at the Southern Theater, and his many different ensemble combinations at his annual Weisman Art Museum concerts.

So many great souls have collaborated with Carei that the list would be endless. I wish I could mention them all here, but you know who you are. Some were great improvisers while others were just starting out. Some played on the street for small change. Some were seasoned performers and some young people or the tiniest children. Some had never improvised before in their lives and were strictly classical players. Always determined that there is supreme art in everybody, Carei gently pushed us into new territory. He has joyfully welcomed unusual instruments and embraced electronic percussionists and sound designers, improvisational dancers, performance painters and poets, healers and shamanic types. Even though his illness seems to have settled Carei a little and caused him to want to work in an ongoing way with various ensembles, basically he has always been a creatively restless spirit, not wanting any ensemble fixed for long, always inviting new people into it or creating totally new groups of instruments, personalities, collaborations. He is the kid in the candy store, saying, I wonder what it would be like to have an oboe and a harp and violin together, and with this and that other instrument. This is the kind of person who will call you up and breathlessly say, "Listen to this, man. I don't know where this came from," and then play it for you over the phone. As I write this, he is still that kid, running to you as if with some beautiful rock he has found. When you look through this book you are really seeing music he wrote for US, his neighborhood, his community, his life.

Always interested in expanding our horizons, he has infiltrated many institutions of higher learning with his heady yet earthy alternative viewpoint, his bag of tricks. At Macalester College, for example, he has worked extensively with Professor of Composition Carlton Macy.

Professor of Piano Donald Betts, and members of the new music ensemble who have played and voyaged and been indoctrinated into his compositional-improvisational schemes, leading to staunch devotees such as pianist and composer Paul Cantrell. Or he will go into schools, community centers, the Children's Museum. I will never forget one morning many years ago at Pillsbury Neighborhood House in Minneapolis, how we made up a piece with tone rows and played it for five little girls, based on the letters of their names, a piece created only for them.

And so, with the same missionary spirit, we hereby present you with the life work of Carei Thomas, one of the most playful and generous artists that has ever graced the universe. Here are traces of the life lights Carei has brought together, unforgettable experiences he's seeded, growth we've all had, performers and listeners alike. Ecumenical, pan-cultural, spiritual, bent on healing and the big picture, pulling us together, truly building the rainbow community, that's Carei. He'd say it is not the result that counts, it is the road itself, what happens along the way. Passing this book on to you is another step on that journey. Take it, let it cajole and inform you, and be glad.

Preface

I consider this publication a 1st Edition and welcome suggestions from readers/musicians regarding revisions for future editions. For those of you who end up playing these compositions, I would like you to make them your own. They are formally mine, but use them as ways to express your own connection to the universe. Improvisations take on the quality of a performer's spirit as you put your spontaneous inspirations into the mix. Many of my songs are written as themes to give structure from which you can define, focus and arrange the content. Feel free to take the source material and infuse it harmonically, temporally, dynamically and culturally, letting it develop organically out of inclusion. Also, not all of the songs are written in Concert. I suspect musicians are going to want to arrange these for their particular instruments and I give permission for them to do so.

The progression of my concepts are not necessarily a linear timeline. My songs also evolved by going back and forth conceptually. This pendulum philosophy is based on the idea of carrying history forward while uniting that which was with the ever-present possibilities of "now time."

This pendulum movement also shows up when my songs illustrate more than one concept. In the Index, I have listed one or two concepts per song, even though some compositions utilize more.

Several of my songs include my Brief Reality concept. Brief Realities are everchanging series of purely invented music often spiced with cells or fragments of written material acting as connective tissue. This gives performers a structure that defines and focuses content while offering a broad choice of source material. Within this tonal order, invention/improvisation ignites the developmental process that creates the true composition and allows it to remain everchangingly fresh. In this process, the songs immediately take on the quality of the performer's spirit and, of course, that cannot be contained totally on the written page. In some songs, such as "Just In Case You Call," the chords are written and the melody is left to the improviser.

Following the Concept Chart are a few pages of descriptions of my compositional concepts. Some of my concept songs started from studies, giving me a way to isolate certain compositional problems I wanted to solve. For example, I had a series of Les Fenetres studies from which my Color Rows came. Then, from my Color Rows, Spiral Building evolved. In the Ruminations section at the end of this book, you'll see some studies from which songs evolved.

A lot of my songs have stories behind them as I am sure is true for most composers. I've included some of those stories in my "Composing/Living" essay.

—Carei F. Thomas

Compositions and Concepts

"Composing/Living"

Carei F. Thomas

I am as much a theorist as a performer/composer. I am enamored by things both micro and macro as in a drop of sea water are all the ingredients of an ocean. I align myself with a cause-and-effect philosophy, exemplifying process and product as one and concluding the journey and destination are the same.

There have been many stages in my development with my compositions going back and forth conceptually from simple songs, to investigations of complex methodologies, to experimentation with mathematical and visual paradigms. This pendulum motion supports my idea of carrying history forward while uniting that which was with the ever-present possibilities of "now time." The purpose of this design is to push new musical ideas forward while keeping history alive.

Some of my concept songs started from studies, giving me a way to isolate certain compositional problems I wanted to solve. Some were developed from my interest in the healing aspects of sound and color. Some were created from rows of algorithmic information and/or arrangements of layered grids or matrices. Some evolved from an interest in multimedia performances, such as my graphic compositions and synth-choral works. Most of my compositions are written to be "runways," designs to offer unique and expansive ways to involve oneself in one's self and in one's reality (environment).

I am also an improviser. I like to use improvisational elements to help instrumentalists free up ways of expressing their connection to the universe. Improvisations take on the quality of the performer's spirit as they put their spontaneous inspirations into the mix. Of course, that cannot be contained on a written page. To give musicians overall direction, I provide algorithmic flow charts along with written themes and narrative descriptions. These give a structure that defines and focuses content while offering a broad choice of source material harmonically, temporally, dynamically and culturally. I choose instrumentalists for what they can "bring" to this process, as they need to partake diligently to infuse and accommodate material that organically develops out of inclusion. Often listeners say they can't differentiate between what is written and what is improvised. In addition, I encourage dialogue in rehearsals and evaluations after concerts, believing out of a geodesic approach comes the learning/relearning and assessment needed to improve the product and progress in a viable continuum.

I love composing, performing and sharing out of the midst of living. "The Boys" was written as I watched my sons, Aairam and Jaahred playing; "Ancestor Energy: Anthem I" was written to accompany a poem of my dear friend, Louis Alemayehu; and "Landing" was written when I went back to Pittsburgh for my Aunt Rebecca's funeral and saw a flock of pigeons circling in the sky. "Pat's Place Saturday" is an autobiographical homage to the place on 35th and Calumet in Chicago where I used to go every Saturday and stay all day and sometimes until early Sunday morning.

"Monsieur Duprée" was written with certain sundry characters in mind who I grew up seeing at the picture show at Saturday matinees: Sidney Greenstreet, Charles Laughton, Orson Welles, Victor Buono, Raymond Burr, and, of late, some of the characters portrayed by the portly Marlon Brando and Forrest Whitaker. It's kind of a cartoon noir character study (with cartoonists Gahan Wilson or Shel Silverstein in mind).

"Magicmysticmaestromentor" is an endearing caricature/portrait study of my friend, Douglas Ewart. It's a march (kind of) and is meant to be all over the place. Douglas' works are kaleidoscopic and his passion for life and the human spirit beams out in a multitude of directions.

"Synescalatoria" uses a minimalistic shifting tonal order—a strobe light effect. This tonal order is designed to accommodate shifting intervallic definitions. This Phononomaly is played until it disintegrates into the true composition, and yet, it is not meant to mimic minimalism techniques.

"Baby, Baby, Home Buddy" hopefully exudes "hominess," like something one might hum in the bathtub or hear coming from the kitchen as a meal is being prepared. It's written to my wife, Joyce Marie, who is my soulmate, my home buddy.

"Accordance" was written the first part of 1998 and then tossed in a corner amongst other compositions. While visiting Paris later that year, I tried it out with David Murray. I sat at his piano and he joined me on tenor . . . too bad we couldn't have recorded that. It was fine. From then on, it's been one of my Amen pieces. It tends to bring folks together all the time and is a fine ending for our evening performances.

"Turn Left, You Can't Miss It" was written after coming back from Kansas City and having visited Charlie Parker's gravesite. It's one of the first compositions that Gary Schulte and I played together and helped solidify our musical friendship.

I'm going to stop there with the song stories and tell you one more life story. In 1993, I was partially paralyzed from Guillain-Barre Syndrome, which has constricted my hands and affected my motor skills. I am grateful I was able to continue composing and using collaborative works of art as vehicles to address sociometry. These vehicles came in the form of Gift Shops (community sharing of gifts) and Unusual Designs and Atypical Settings (UDAS) events. Gift Shops are also designed to encourage leadership through value creation where we all attack and chase the shadows from the daylight with our collaborations. UDAS events often include explorations of experimental music. Often stories are weaved in and out of the performances and the songs that result become rich testimonies of the communities from which they came. I feel a lot of this happened, as well, when I was growing up in the Hill District of Pittsburgh, Pennsylvania. Filled with the richness of history and cultures, I had an early start in discerning vital connections that reinforce values.

I hope some of what I have presented in this book will spark other theorists to look at their own historically unique concepts and help them see how their contributions enrich their colleagues and communities. Instrumentalists, do with the "charts" as you see fit in creating the "true" composition and have fun with them. And, students, I hope you experience music as an art form that bolsters the human spirit, as you utilize your cognitive, creative and psychomotor skills. The best to you!

In conclusion, I would like to share this poem, written in 2000, entitled "Alone in the Helix, Too."

ALONE IN THE HELIX, TOO

This thing that's already DONE
Makes no references
Amends all irony while continuing to unwind . . .

How sweet this CHANGE, this LIGHT
And
DARKNESS, which turns/returns all circles into spirals of
Unfolding color yet to be named . . .

. . . Making each "brief reality" a treasure, a divine protection,
which teaches US to nurture the brilliance and candor of each

"LIFE'S MOMENT"

Another precious thing born without wings . . .

ALWHERE

CAREI THOMAS
COMPOSITIONAL CONCEPTS CHART

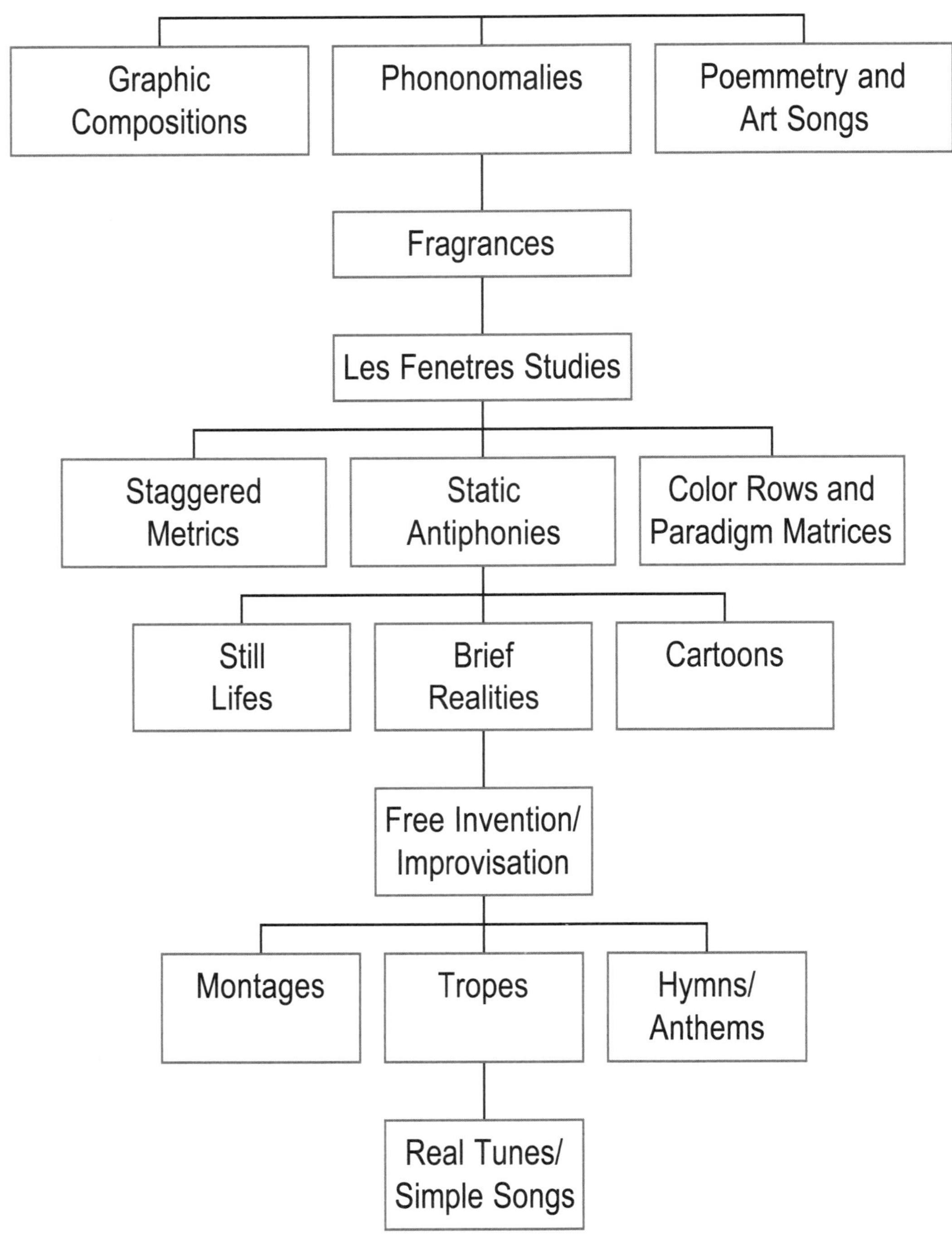

Description of Concepts

Real Tunes/Simple Songs were the elements of my first compositions. They were just that—real tunes and simple songs. Improvisation was provided for within the harmonic structure of the chord progressions. These include songs with particular orientations or qualities, such as jazz, classical, passacaglias, waltzes, circle songs, ballads, elegies, gigues, saudades and gymnopedies.

Montages, Tropes, and Hymns/Anthems were largely written in the next stage of my development. This phase partly came from my fascination with the folkloric quality of melodies—both the simple and irregular constructions.

> **Montages** are sonic collages—similar to those montages seen in nature and visual art works. They rely on disparate patches of harmonic and melodic material interfacing and transmuting tone and harmonic definition to form a complete piece of music.
>
> **Tropes** evolved out of my penchant for Gregorian Chants and the works of Machaut, DuFay, and Pergolesi. They are simple modal-influenced pieces in which I wanted to use fresh harmonic designs. They have varying scale relationships and staggered metric systems with a propensity towards Plainsong elements.
>
> **Hymns/Anthems** are just that—hymns and anthems, sometimes elegy-like, sometimes with a saudade quality.

Free Invention/Improvisation was developed and actualized at the Rainbow Gallery in Minneapolis in the 1970s. This was a natural progression from the Chicago time I spent with Kalaparush Maurice McIntyre and Wadada Leo Smith in the late 1960s. At the Rainbow Gallery I had the opportunity to work ongoingly on my music with groups of musicians and began to realize the way I would be composing in the future.

Still Lifes, Brief Realities, and Cartoons have written references in them but improvisation is their most important element. These compositions require new scoring techniques (i.e., flow charts, narrative descriptions, and manuscript reductions) and can have placement of people with varying musical abilities, including amateurs, aspirants and professionals.

Still Lifes are precursors of my Fragrance compositions. They are usually Largo/Lento in tempo and hang like frozen moments in time. Still Lifes draw from a minimalistic expansion and diminution of tonal and metric definition like light that is reflected off a revolving ballroom sphere—stately, yet whimsical and sparkling.

Brief Realities became a foundational concept of much that has followed in my composing career. They are ever-changing series of purely invented music often spiced with cells or fragments of written material acting like connective tissue. I feel this improvisational concept gives performers a structure that defines and focuses content while offering a broad choice of source material. Within this tonal order, invention/improvisation ignites the developmental process that creates the true composition and allows it to remain everchangingly fresh. My Brief Reality compositions seek out and call for exemplary instrumentalists to infuse or accommodate fabric or material that organically develops out of inclusion.

Cartoons convey a slapstick humorous quality and allow or suggest to the instrumentalist(s) to snatch fragments of thematic material and expand it harmonically, temporally, dynamically, and culturally. These are learned the way "doo-wop" singing groups in my inner-city neighborhood learned songs—by doing them over and over until, voilá, the piece is born. They can aurally display something "Cubist" in nature, like the visuals of Braque, Picasso, or Bearden. Cartoons can also be march-like at times and/or have caricature qualities.

Staggered Metrics, Static Antiphonies, and Color Rows/Paradigm Matrices were all in the next stage of my compositional development. They are controlled improvisational concepts or techniques which allow for a broader expansion of metric designs and tonal displacement.

Staggered Metrics stagger the metric system. They tie into Static Antiphonies and Color Rows and become a foundation for the development of Paradigm Matrices. Staggered Metrics are a succession of measures with varying metric designs (i.e., 3/4, 7/4, 2/4, 5/4, 7/4, etc., so the beats—here 24—can equal 6 measures of 4/4 or 4 measures of 6/4, etc.). This can give a varying pulse and inference of accent to the whole piece. In some songs the staggered metrics shift in a patterned, planned way such as in the piece entitled "Helix."

Static Antiphonies use a configuration of "♒ ♒" I call these symbols "scrambles." They prompt instrumentalists to freely improvise with little thought of tonality but rather with an emphasis on timbre and emotional expression. Then, I add metric considerations. A number within a scramble designates its duration (i.e., ♒ ♒ with a 4 in it [♒ 4 ♒] equals four beats of free invention).

Color Rows/Paradigm Matrices were developed from my interest in the healing aspects of sound and color. They draw on a harmonic concept to coordinate sound, tonality and color in compositional fabric, achieving a dreamscape atmosphere as vast as the sky, ever-changing and timeless. Color Rows are compositions created from rows of information. Sometimes I referred to them as Spiral Building. Compositions can be drawn from the alphabet using a grid (matrix). A more advanced composition develops when metric considerations are added. A number above a note designates its duration (i.e., E with a 2 above it is E held for two beats). Instrumentalists have a choice of register (G can be realized as G3 - G2, etc.). Paradigm Matrices are uses of the above development but they are arranged in a more layered grid or in stacks of information. One of these is created from using the alphabet in a grid (matrix) as follows:

A	B	C	D	E	F	G
H	I	J	K	L	M	N
O	P	Q	R	S	T	U
V	W	X	Y	Z		

As we all know (in standard notation), there isn't any note "H" or "M," etc. In this composition, I've replaced those letters with half step ascending musical increments. For example, under the letter A, progressing downward vertically, H becomes A#—O becomes B—V becomes C, etc.

A	B	C	D	E	F	G
A#	C	C#	D#	F	F#	G#
B	C#	D	E	F#	G	A
C	D	D#	F	G		

Having permutated the alphabet with the above notes from H through Z, the composition is then developed thusly:

T	H	R	E	E	B	A	G	S		F	U	L	L
G	A#	E	E	E	B	A	G	F#		F	A	F	F

A more advanced composition would add metric considerations. A number above a note designates its duration (i.e., E with a 2 above it is E held for two beats). Instrumentalists have a choice of register (G can be realized as G3—G2, etc.).

T	H	R	E	E	B	A	G	S		F	U	L	L
	4	3				3	2					2	
G	A#	E	E	E	B	A	G	F#		F	A	F	F

Les Fenetres Studies were a vehicle by which I realized some of my earlier concepts. I had a group called Les Fenetres which provided the "window" for developing these studies.

Fragrances are compositions that utilize the preceding concepts and also are a culmination of them. These compositions are panharmonic/pantonal/pandurational in nature. They exude a redolent quality achieved through interesting harmonic and tonal designs but are, for the most part, Real Tunes/Simple Songs—lending themselves to a vaporous mercurial essence. They marry the avant-garde and the lyrical in ballad form. Fragrances are intuitive structures with an efflorescence of spontaneity grounded in a proven history of musical evolution.

Graphic Compositions, Phononomalies, Poemmetry and Art Songs have become a part of my more recent compositional style due to interest in multimedia performances. This multimedia direction has allowed me to draw on and expand upon earlier techniques, to rekindle ideas and give them new directions, and to have my art form be more than a performance/spectator one.

I have done eight **Graphic Compositions** and used them in concerts. From the graphics, musicians have a base for their interpretative inventions/improvisations. The graphics can be projected on varying grounds (i.e., folded, hanging or windblown fabric, or irregular surfaces) and used with sound design as a ground for contemporary dance. And, when the graphics are done in sculpture form, artists and/or audiences can interact with them. My graphic compositions are presented in the Ruminations.

Phononomalies were developed when I added to my work the "smoke and mirrors" of acoustical/electronic music. I have developed these tonal fabrics (sound designs) to be used as a canvas accommodating the collaborative endeavors of poetry, spoken word, dance, video, visual art forms, and theatre—along with their closest friend . . . Silence. The first of these were done with a group I call Sound Window(s). To date, we have done five Sound Window(s) concerts. These have been experimental sound studies using voice, acoustical instruments, and electronic instrumentation for a quartet ensemble. Each of the four "windows" are peered through by its neighboring self/selves in a kaleidoscopic linear/dynamic way. My Photochromokinesis songs are forms of phononomalies that have elements of light, color and movement in them. Photochromokinesis might suggest something clinically mystical, but like so many things complex, it's simply pretty. I do think/feel/sense a changing of musical light and color in these pieces and often a hypnotic refraction-like quality that nudges soloists and audiences to bath in a brief reality of this photochromokinesis experience.

Poemmetry is a spatial-kinetic-music-word concept. It is using words, phrases and onomatopoetic expressions in a raconteur fashion or in conjunction with larger developed works. The participant(s) can take on varying formations (dyads, triads, etc.). Poemmetry utilizes poetry and the audience in making the compositional fabric work. I've also written several **Art Songs** which have been written for use in multi-disciplined performances, such as "Gardens of My Ancestors, "Depot," and "Familiar Fields of Ghandi, King and Ikeda" (performed with poetry and spoken word), "Accordance" (which has words to be sung), "Cool Billy Dude" (used with theater), and "Ordinaire" (written for synth-chorus).

Alphabetical Song Listing

Page	Song Title	Concept	Year
73	Beatrice Hamilton/Momma Whatnow: Trope IV	Trope	1978
74	Beaujaullé	Simple Song	1985
75	Bird Symbols	Simple Song	1988
76	Birthday Montage for Mahrni and Joi: Montage I	Montage	1979
79	Birthday Montage: 1-19-48: Montage IX	Montage	1986
80	Blue Light Phononomaly for Beauford	Phononomaly	2005
83	Bon Visage: Meridel/Etta	Simple Song	1986
84	Both Sides of the Issue: Cartoons Out of Monk I	Cartoon	2002
86	Buhne: Sundae Fance with Nance	Simple Song	1979
88	But Then, The Kings (Dedicated to Carla Bley) Cartoon VII	Cartoon	1979
89	Careiin' a Slight Monkin': Cartoons Out of Monk V	Cartoon	2002
92	Careyin' a Slight Birdin'	Simple Song	1969
93	Certain Peace/Silk Road (Dedicated to Daisaku Ikeda)	Simple Song	1977
97	Charles Donald Joseph Angus McLean, Jr.: Trope II	Trope	1978
99	Chuckles': Cartoons Out of Monk III	Cartoon	2002
101	Cjalme: Fragrance XIV	Fragrance	2003
102	Cool Billy Dude	Art Song	1999
103	Depot	Art Song	2003
109	Dey's Still Not Satisfied: Cartoons Out of Monk II	Cartoon	2002
110	Ditto . . . Comma: Les Fenetres Studie 8	Color Rows, Cartoon	1988
112	Donald 'n' Faye	Simple Song	2003
113	Down and Out Our Way: Cartoon IX	Cartoon	2001
115	E.K.E. (Edward Kennedy Ellington): Drexel Boulevard Elegy	Simple Song (Elegy)	1986
116	Enchantment	Simple Song (Waltz)	1988
117	Euterpreuse: Fragrance XV	Fragrance	2003
118	Everybody Knows: Montage IV	Montages, Simple Song	1984
119	Familiar Fields	Simple Song	1985

Page	Song Title	Concept	Year
120	Finally Baby Baby	Simple Song (Ballad)	1998
124	Fluster the Cat: Cartoon II	Cartoon	1979
125	GI . GO (Garbage In . Garbage Out)	Simple Song	1988
126	Helix	Phononomaly	1988
127	Hello Rahsaan . . . Hello Eric: Cartoon III	Cartoon	1977
128	Hidden Peaces	Still Life	2002
129	Hints . . . Glimpses	Simple Song	1978
133	Hittin' the Silk	Simple Song (Ballad)	1962
134	Home Clean	Simple Song (Ballad)	1979
136	I Didn't: Sentempathy I	Art Song	1978
137	Ibidem	Static Antiphony	2004
138	Inspiration: After Aairam's Letter	Simple Song	1990–2009
140	Interpenetration: Fresh Air of Majesta: Fragrance VII	Fragrance	1992–2007
142	Just In Case You Call	Simple Song (Ballad)	1989
143	Jy'laahorlx: Fragrance XX	Fragrance	2004
146	Kansas City Déjà Vu	Simple Song	1979
147	Kind Ones/Bright Faith	Simple Song (Ballad)	1977
148	Kwitchurbeliakin: Cartoon VI	Cartoon	1980
149	Lady Don't Hang Yo' Head Down So Low or Eventually You're Gonna Crack Yo' Spine	Simple Song/Still Life	1979
150	Landing	Anthem	2008
151	Lil' Granny's Chariot Come	Simple Song	1964
152	Look Alikes	Simple Song	1992
156	Magicmysticmaestromentor: Cartoon X	Color Rows, Cartoon	1992
157	Mary Lou's Chihuly	Simple Song	2007
159	Memory (Dedicated to Frank Thomas)	Simple Song (Ballad), Staggered Metrics	1989
163	Minuet for Donna: Gymnopedie I	Simple Song	1979
164	Mississippi Gentleman Travel'n: Cartoons Out of Monk IV	Cartoon	2002

Page	Song Title	Concept	Year
165	Mom Mary's Troux Bloux Roux	Simple Song	2002
168	Monsieur Duprée: Cartoon XV	Cartoon, Color Rows	2000
170	My Early 'Trane of Thought	Simple Song	1962
173	My Fifth Step During Eclipse: Montage II	Simple Song	1979
174	New Same Sweet	Simple Song	2009
175	No New News Blues/Kohoutek	Simple Song	1976
176	Noir In Purple (Dedicated to Thelonius Monk, Mal Waldron, and Chopin)	Simple Song	1986
177	Nothing Personal	Simple Song (Passacaglia)	1986
178	Nys	Simple Song	1978
179	Of Families and Friends	Simple Song	1977
180	Of Times Old and New: Trope VI	Trope	2003
181	One Final Answer: Photochromokinesis IV	Phononomaly	2006
192	One True Essence of Grümbelmüüch: Fragrance V	Staggered Metrics, Fragrance	1993
195	Opalessence/Chiron: Les Fenetres Studie 9	Color Rows	1988
196	Our Tryst Waltz	Simple Song	1979
198	Pat's Place Saturdays	Simple Song	1966
199	Precious Waltz	Simple Song (Waltz)	1983
200	Quesyi	Simple Song	1978
201	Quiet By Now	Simple Song	2004
204	Quippihd: Fragrance XIII	Fragrance	2003
206	Rhyssaal: Fragrance XVIII	Fragrance	2003
209	Roagjyii-Ahl: Fragrance XII	Fragrance	2001
210	Robert Fitzgerald/Home Early: Trope I	Trope	1978
211	Sentempathy	Simple Song (Ballad)	1992
212	Sh-h-h! This is the Best Part	Color Rows	2003
215	Simile I	Cartoon	2002
217	Sir Martin of Upton Heights/Martin Mumbleau: Trope III	Trope	1978
223	Sky: Les Fenetres Studie 6	Color Rows	1996

Page	Song Title	Concept	Year
224	Slymn Hymn	Hymn	1991
227	Spanky	Cartoon	1962
229	Steps: Anthem V	Anthem	2000
233	Still Time	Simple Song (Ballad), Still Life	1991
235	Story Line: Everyone's on Their Way Home	Staggered Metrics (Ballad)	1988
236	Swe' Potatah: An Old Jazz Song for Bennie and Wayne	Simple Song	1990
237	Synescalatoria	Phononomaly	2004
238	Thank You Mother, Thank You Father	Simple Song (Ballad)	1978
239	That Poignant Scent of Will (Dedicated to Billie Holiday) Fragrance IV	Fragrance	1992
240	The Boys, Jaahri and Aairam: Cartoon IV	Cartoon	1979
243	The Girls at Gröensbürgwalstraat 27	Simple Song	1962
244	The Valentine's Day	Montage, Simple Song	2003
245	The Valley, The Shadow and The Light: Gymnopedie II	Staggered Metrics, Still Life	1989
246	There, Off Yonder: Cartoon I	Cartoon	1969
247	This Allegiance: Anthem VI	Anthem	2003
250	This Time Last Spring	Simple Song	1981
251	Tippy One Ahead	Static Antiphony	2002
252	TOT	Simple Song	1986
256	Treasured Alliances	Phononomaly	2001
257	Treasures	Simple Song	1978
258	Triad	Still Life, Cartoon	1979
260	Tryptycht for Molly	Simple Song	1978
261	Tryxsisia: Gymnopedie III	Simple Song	2003
263	Tsimtsum: Photochromokinesis III	Phononomaly	2001
265	Turn Left, You Can't Miss It: Montage III	Montage	1979
266	Turning Point Anthem: Anthem II	Anthem	1979
267	When Where Is Lost	Brief Reality	2001

Page	Song Title	Concept	Year
268	Wraith Dance: Les Fenetres Studie 7	Color Rows	1988
269	You Bet Your Life/That's Shu Biz	Simple Song	1962
270	You I Love	Simple Song	2002

GRAPHIC COMPOSITIONS

Page	Song Title	Year
276	Ends Open for the Female in Me (Dedicated to M.C. Escher)	1983
277	Nimbus	1983
278	Roy McBride in Four Places	1983
279	She/Woman	1983
280	Snellie	1983
281	Sound Town I	1983
282	Sound Town II	1983
283	The Day—Mimi	1983

SYNTH-CHORAL WORKS

Page	Song Title	Year
286	Baahmidjian Scaal	2007
289	Familiar Fields	2007
292	Fresh Air of Majesta	2007
296	HIdden Peaces	2007
297	Helix for Spiral Building I	2007
301	Kind Peace	2007
303	Ordinaire	2007
308	Slymn Hymn	2007

RUMINATIONS

Page	Song Title	Concept	Year
317	Alwhere	Anthem	1989
318	Alwhere (Static Antiphony)	Static Antiphony	1989
319	Cartoon Fragma	Cartoon	1985
322	Choose Choice	Still Life	1980
323	Color Rows for Spiral Building	Color Rows (Pre Fragrance)	1985
326	Colorscape Matrix	Matrix	1997
327	Crowding Daylight	Matrix	1997
328	De Facto	Matrix	1980
329	Dream for Times Out of Mind	Staggered Metrics, Paradigm Matrices	1988
333	Eric Only Knew	Still Life	2000
334	From Five on Down with Four	Staggered Metrics	1967
335	Glide I and Glide II	Color Rows	2000
336	Heirloom	Simple Song	1962
337	If You Ask Me	Still Life	1983
338	Juxtaportation	Phononomoly	1997
339	Kandinsky Lights to Dream On	Photochromokinesis II	1985
345	Kandinsky Static Antiphony	Static Antiphony	2000
346	Live Wire	(Early Trope)	1977
347	Magicmysticmaestromentor	Cartoon X (Color Rows)	1992
349	Morse Code	Poemmetry	1996
350	Nolemon|nomeloN	Matrix Palindromic)	1999
351	Paradigm I	Matrix	1983
352	Period	Brief Reality, Staggered Metrics	1983
353	Poemmetry	Poemmetry	1993
354	Side Show Color Row	Cartoon, Color Rows, Matrix	2000
355	Sky Extensions: Les Fenetres Studie 6	Color Rows	1996

SONGS

A Fragrance of Distant Sundays

A Fragrance of Distant Sundays (Continued)

A Fragrance of Distant Sundays (Continued)

A Fragrance of Distant Sundays (Continued)

A Fragrance of Distant Sundays (Continued)

A Tear in November

Accordance

© 1997 Carei F. Thomas
concert pitch
C G F D♭ C C G A
D9 G7 C G F D♭ C
F G C D9 G7 C G7
G7 C F C C F C
D D G D7 G
G F G7 C G F D♭ C C G C
D9 G7 C G F F C F G C
D9 G7 C F C

Accordance/Love One Another

© 1997, 2005 Carei F. Thomas and Mary L. Roark

Permission given by Mike Roark and Lisa Haner (Mary's children) to include lyrics of Mary Roark, which became the song "Love One Another."

Accordance/Love One Another (Continued)

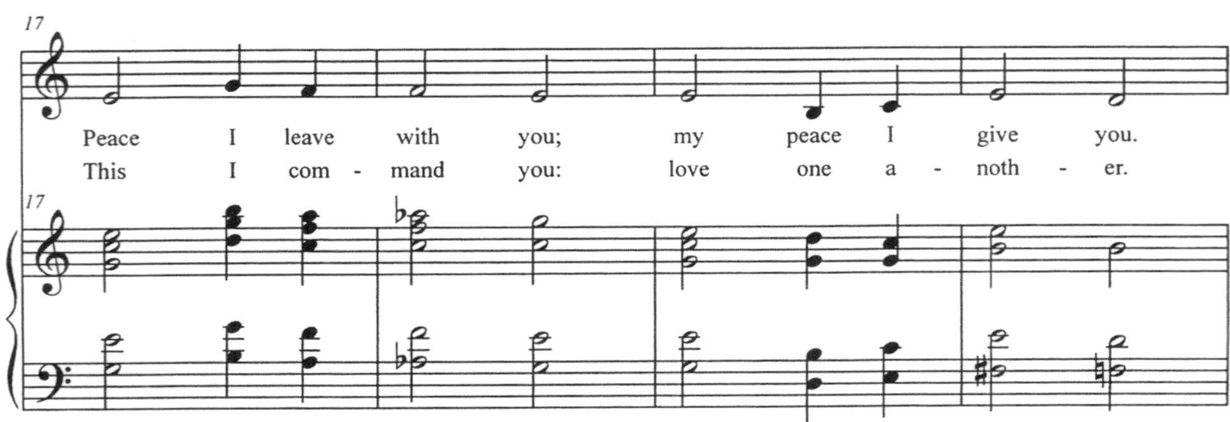

After Sunday Morning's Conversation

Ages'

Ages' (Continued)

Ages' (Continued)

Ages' (Optional Solo Sequence Field)

© 1969 Carei F. Thomas
Arranger

Ages' (Optional Solo Sequence Field) (Continued)

© 1969 Carei F. Thomas
Arranger

Ahead From the Past

Ballad

© 1993 Carei F. Thomas

Ahead From the Past (Continued)

Alwhere

Flute
Piano
Gm9
Am9
Em9
BbM7
Ab7#9 b13
D7#9 b13
E7#9 b13
4
Fl.
Pno.
Db7#9 b13
B7#9 b13
Gb7#9
B7#9 b13
FM#11
BbM#11

Alwhere (Continued)

Alwhere (Continued)

Alwhere (Continued)

Amaryllis/Atlantis Calling

An Old Child's Saying

An Old Child's Saying (Continued)

An Old Child's Saying (Continued)

An Old Wise Tale

Ancestor Energy: Anthem I

And In the Meantime: Fragrance IXa

Oboe

Bass Clarinet

Vibraphone

Piano

Violin

Violoncello

Contrabass

And In the Meantime: Fragrance IXa (Continued)

And In the Meantime: Fragrance IXa (Continued)

And In the Meantime: Fragrance IXa (Continued)

16

Ob.

B. Cl.

16

Vib.

16

Pno.

16

Vln.

Vc.

Cb.

And In the Meantime: Fragrance IXa (Continued)

And In the Meantime: Fragrance IXa (Continued)

Improvisational Progression: Measures 30–33 (Chord Changes to Solo upon). Then recap theme for ending.

And In the Meantime: Fragrance IXa (Continued)

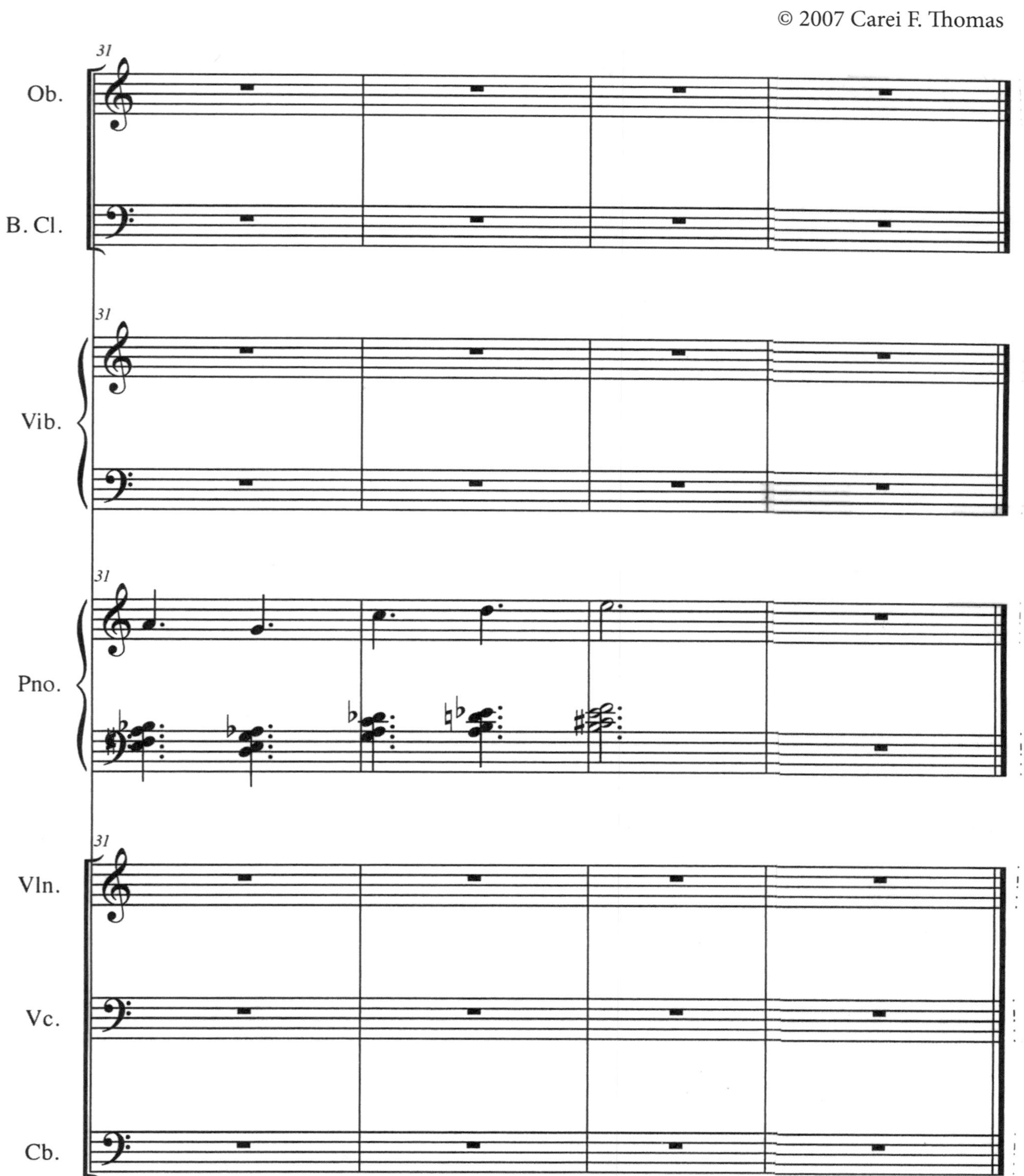

Anna and Alfred's Peace

Anna and Alfred's Peace (Continued)

Anna and Alfred's Peace (Continued)

Anna and Alfred's Peace (Continued)

30
T. Sx.

30
Tba.

30
Pno.

Another Castle

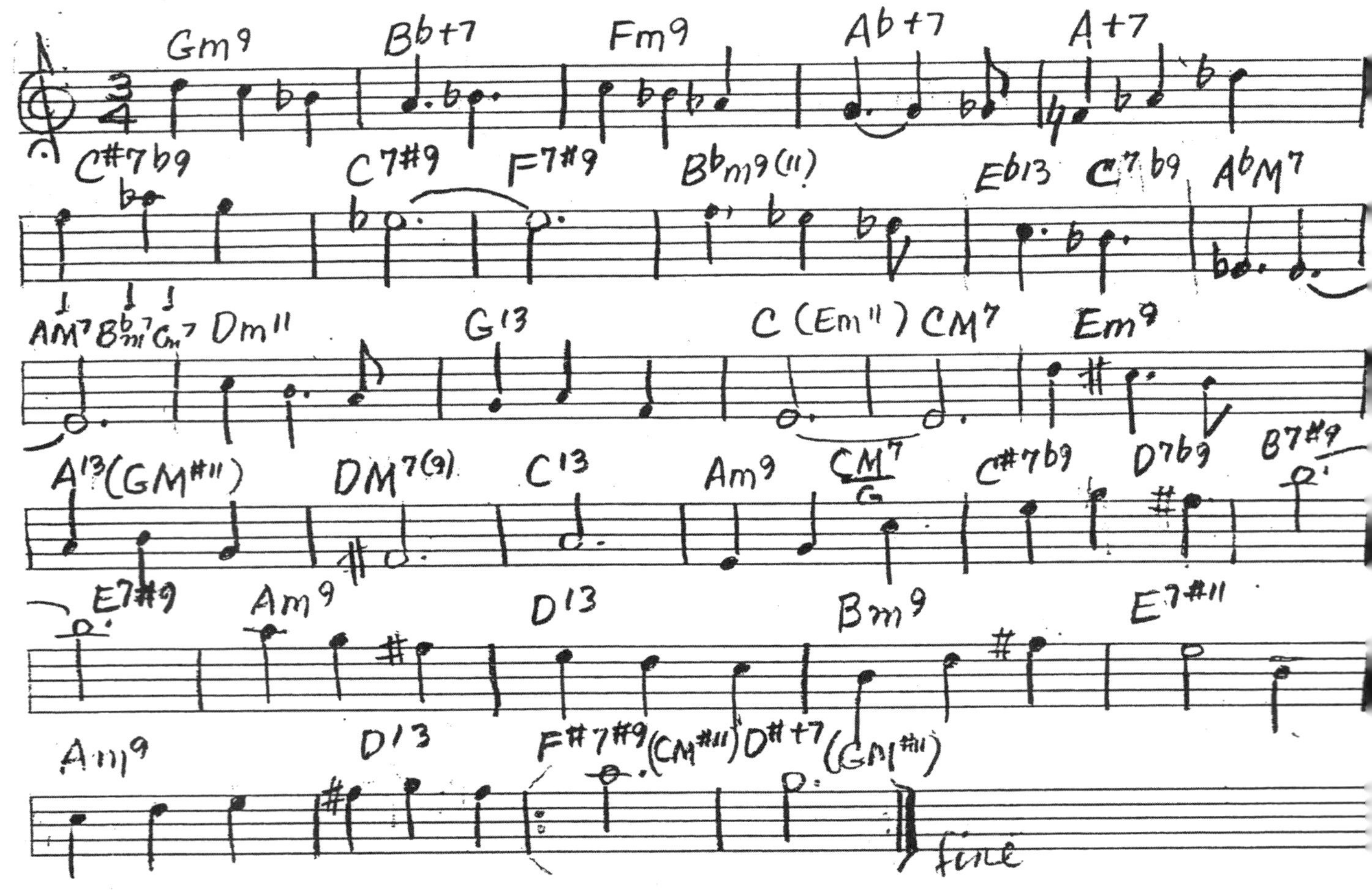

Apple/Orange (The Ole Elk's Ball)

Apple/Orange (Continued)

Arriving at Ten

Atrixity

Atypical Autumn Seasoning

Atypical Autumn Seasoning (Continued)

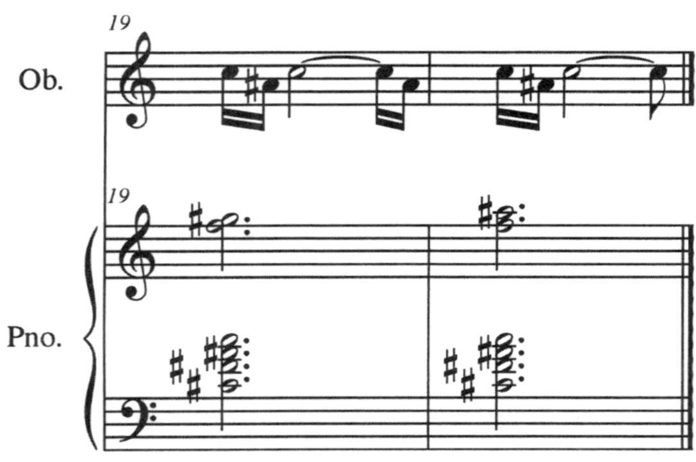

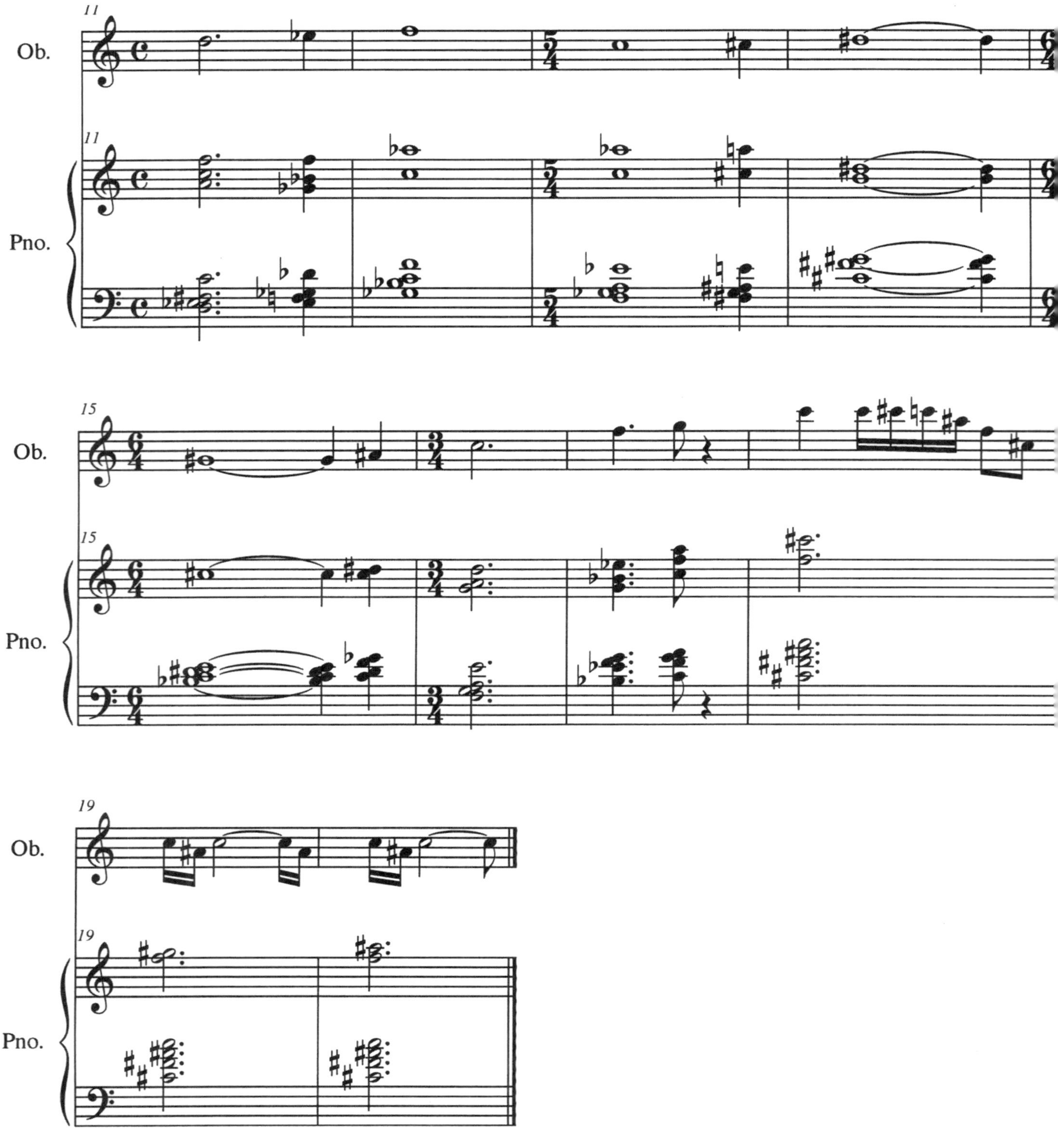
11
Ob.
11
Pno.
15
Ob.
15
Pno.
19
Ob.
19
Pno.

Awestruck Waters of Antiquity

Awestruck Waters of Antiquity (Continued)

Baahmidjian Scaal

Baby Baby/Home Buddy

Baby Baby/Home Buddy (Continued)

Baby Baby's Birthday Waltz

Baby Baby's Birthday Waltz (Continued)

Basic 'Traneing

Beatrice Hamilton/Momma Whatnow

Beaujaullé

GbM#11 BM#11 D7#9b5 F7#9 Ab7#9 F7#9 Db7#9b13 CM#11
CM#11 CM#11 CM#11 BbM#11 EbM#11 F#7#9b5 A7#9 C7b9 A7b9
A+7 DM#11 DM#11 EM#11 EM#11 A°#7 B°#7
Gb13 A°#7 C#°#7 Gb7 Ab+7 FM#11 FM#11 GbM#11 BM#11
D7#9b5 F7#9 D13 Bb13 Eb13 EbM#11 EbM#11 EbM#11 EbM#11
fine

Bird Symbols

Birthday Montage for Mahrni and Joi

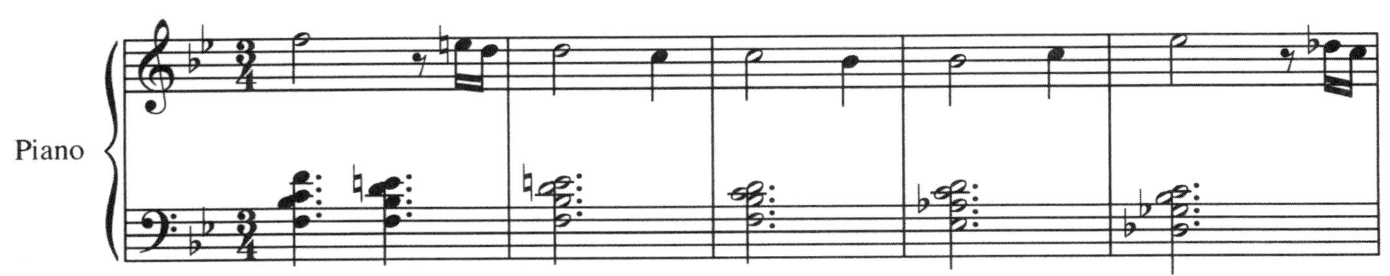

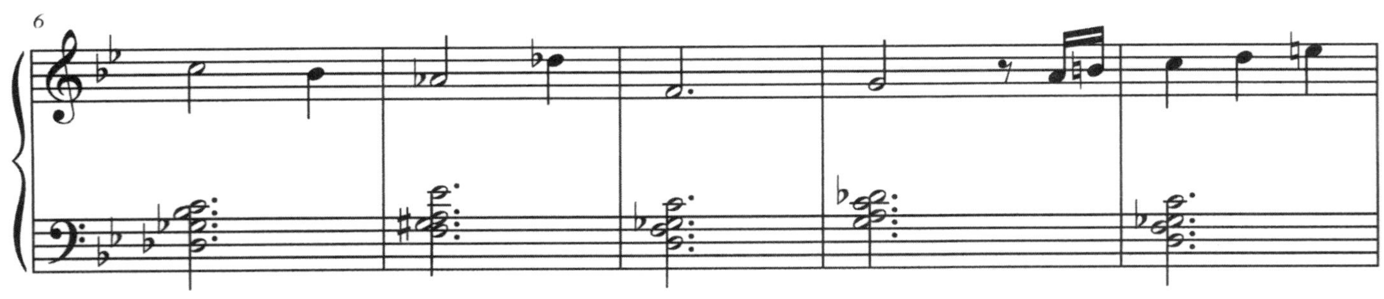

Birthday Montage for Mahrni and Joi (Continued)

Birthday Montage for Mahrni and Joi (Continued)

46

51

56

61

Birthday Montage: 1-19-48

Blue Light Phononomaly for Beauford

This piece was written specifically for and dedicated to the Zeitgeist Ensemble.

Patrick O'Keefe decided, after rehearsing it with Bb Clarinet, to perform it with Bass Clarinet. Turns out, I am glad he did! ☺

The piano and cello enter and spice the piece with fragments of timbral nuance.

Blue Light Phononomaly for Beauford (Continued)

Blue Light Phononomaly for Beauford (Continued)

Bon Visage: Meridel/Etta

concert pitch

Both Sides of the Issue

Both Sides of the Issue (Continued)

Buhne: Sundae Fance with Nance

Buhne: Sundae Fance with Nance (Continued)

But Then, The Kings
(Dedicated to Carla Bley)

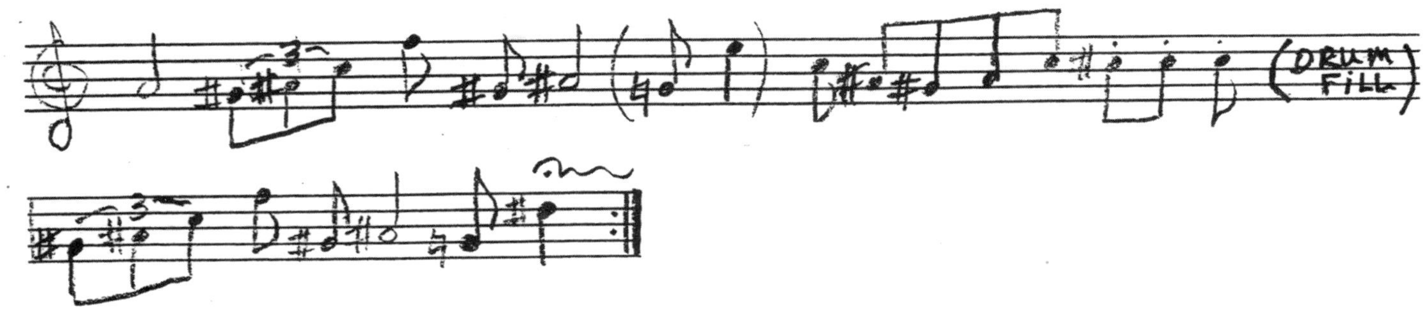

Carla penned an interesting, cartoonesque rendering called "And Now, The Queen," which is similar but different on examination to this "But Then, The Kings." You might want to search out Carla's "And Now, the Queen" and maybe put these two together or nada-nada-nada. Maybe spice it with some color rows or other interesting improvisational variants.

I've always been fascinated with Carla and Paul Bley, Anne Peacock and Brad Mehldau; the way they dance and prance with metrics and melodies—no light; no darkness.

Careiin' a Slight Monkin'

Alto Saxophone

Flugelhorn

Baritone

Piano

Careiin' a Slight Monkin' (Continued)

Careiin' a Slight Monkin' (Continued)

Careyin' a Slight Birdin'

Certain Peace/Silk Road
(Dedicated to Daisaku Ikeda)

Certain Peace/Silk Road (Continued)

Certain Peace/Silk Road (Continued)

Certain Peace/Silk Road (Continued)

Charles Donald Joseph Angus McLean, Jr.

Charles Donald Joseph Angus McLean, Jr. (Continued)

Chuckles'

Piano
B♭7 C7 E♭7
D♭7 D7 D♭7 D7
3
Pno.
B♭7 C7 E♭7
D♭7 D7 D♭7 D7
5
Pno.
E♭7
A♭7
E♭M6
8
Pno.
G7
C7
E7

Chuckles' (Continued)

Makes me think of a Derby-wearing, El Producto cigar smoking, diamond-on-the-pinky finger, pinstriped, tabbed-collar-shirt bedecked character, in some old New Orleanian bar, known for making Fahrenheit and Celsius a happy marriage of hot and sweat.

Cjalmė

Cool Billy Dude

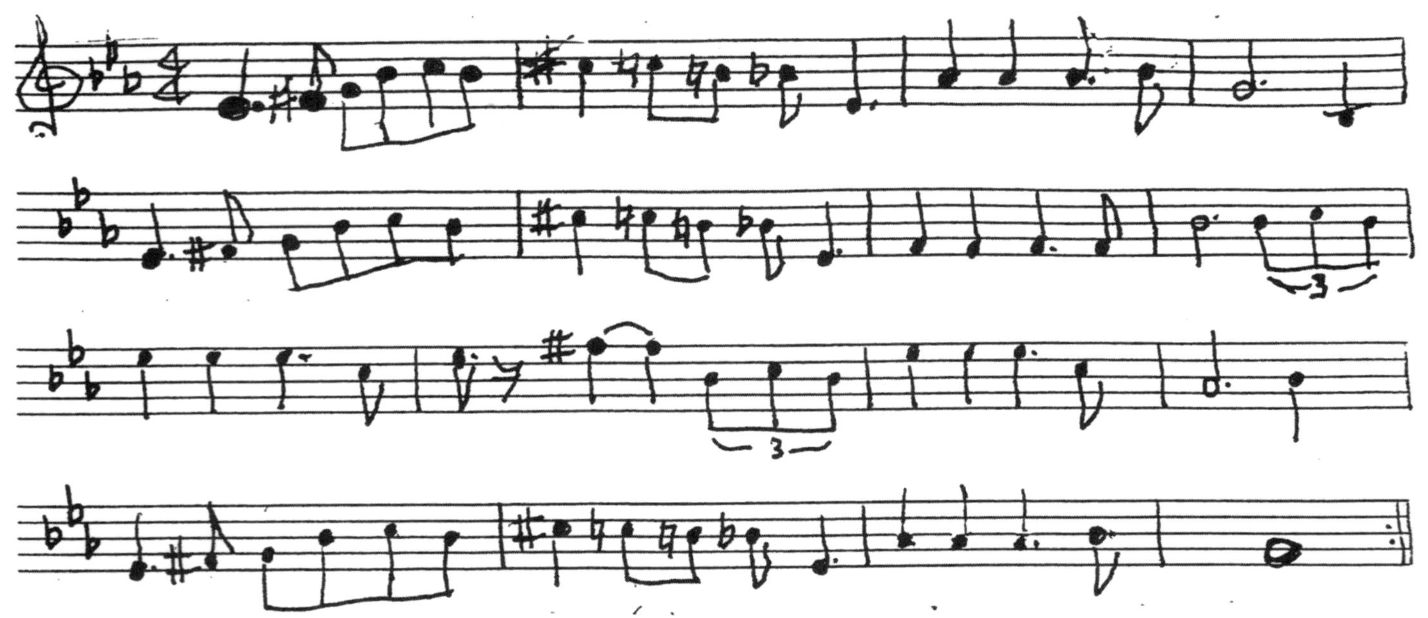

Russ Freeman, pianist in the Chet Baker heydays comes to mind, as well as some Ry Cooder character. A mid-sixties Minneapolis West Bank caricature study. Just right for Interact Theater's "A Day In The Life of Interact."

Depot

Piano
Bass
Light is sel - dom dis - cerned a - lone as a
Violin
4
Pno.
B
friend of dark - ne - ess yet out of hu-mil - i - ty
Vln.

Depot (Continued)

Depot (Continued)

Depot (Continued)

Depot (Continued)

27

Pno.

27

B

ter - nal Hymn ________ N - o re-fren

27

Vln.

30

Pno.

30

B

ces nec-ess-ar - y________ NO - O - LIGHT

30

Vln.

Depot (Continued)

Dey's Still Not Satisfied

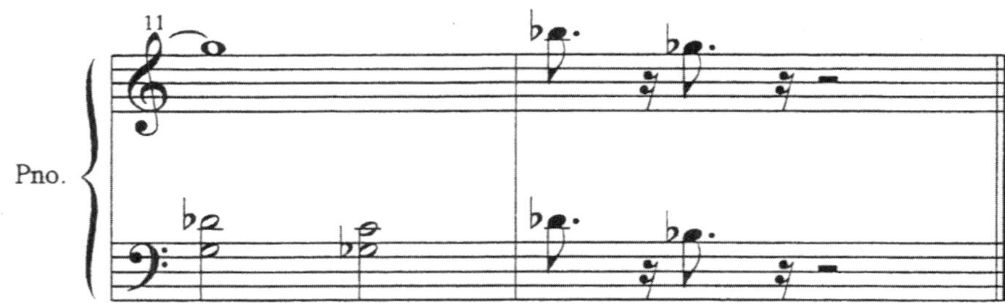

Ditto . . . Comma

Alto Sax.
Tenor Sax.
Trumpet in B♭
Acoustic Bass
Piano
A. Sx.
T. Sx.
B♭ Tpt.
A.B.
Pno.

Ditto . . . Comma (Continued)

A march full of political chutzpah conjured up by topical TV newscasts out to get the best ratings. For some reason it doesn't replace "EXTRA, EXTRA, READ ALL ABOUT IT" for me. CNN, MSNBC, FOX, etc., all doin' the screwy dance with "our" reality so we can keep up with what's going on in "their " world . . . now add blogs and twitter, and voilá—a new norm; cunning disambiguation?

Donald 'n' Faye

Down and Out Our Way

Down and Out Our Way (Continued)

While growing up in Pittsburgh, I was enamoured by the universal messages that floated to the top of the neighborhood-enriched cartoons by J.R. Williams appearing in a local newspaper. These, like Fontaine Fox's Toonerville Trolley (an animated cartoon), Lil' Rascals, Our Gang, and Bowery Boys evoked this friendship/camaraderie thing that bonds neighbors/humanity irregardless of culture, class, race, etc. This song reminds me of my precious connection to my first "hood" and how I've sought out those warm snuggly feelings in all the neighborhoods that followed . . . 'til now it's like this UNIVERSE IS ONE GREAT BIG NEIGHBORHOOD and we/I'm connected to it. The commonality of the situations Williams presented make it possible for people to easily recognize themselves and relish in the feelings of being different and being the same.

E.K.E. (Edward Kennedy Ellington) Drexel Boulevard Elegy

Enchantment

Euterpreuse

Everybody Knows

Sentimentality. Kinda makes me remember those times I had to recite a part in a holiday play my dear Aunt Rebecca was directing at Ebenezer Baptist Church in Pittsburgh, or the "shy-shine" that accompanied me on my first date, or when I sang "Since I Fell for You" in front of Mr. Manfred Sales and the Boy Scouts Troop 59 talent review, or when I said the "wrong thing" at the dinner table among family and guests.

Familiar Fields

Finally Baby Baby

Finally Baby Baby (Continued)

Finally Baby Baby (Continued)

Finally Baby Baby (Continued)

Fluster the Cat

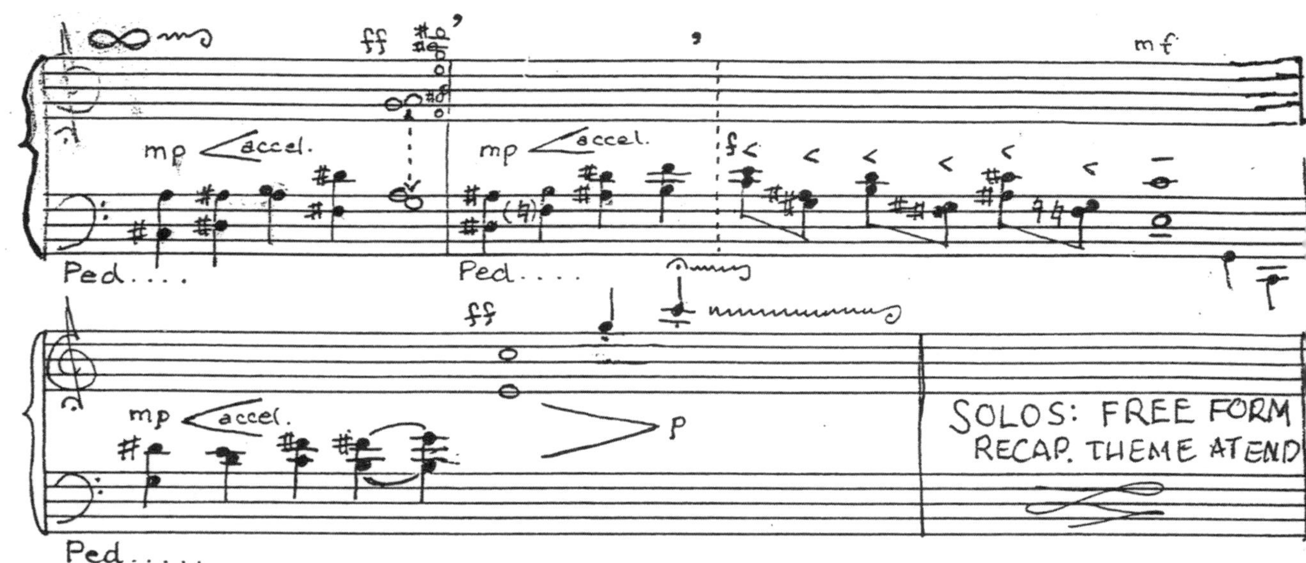

Written for/about "Fluffy," my kids' first pet, an orange tabby cat. My daughter Joi and "Fluster" as he was alternatively called ruled the domain at times. He composed these "wonderful" songs or would just lounge-out on the upper register of our old Cable Nelson. His tail was full of "accent mojo."

GI . GO (Garbage In . Garbage Out)

Helix

Analyze/Study/Expand

(See "Helix for Spiral Building I" in the Synth-Choral section for further ideas.)

Hello Rahsaan . . . Hello Eric

Hidden Peaces

Hints . . . Glimpses

Latino / Cha Cha

DM7(9) | Bm9 | FM#11

FM#11 | E7#9 | E7#9 | Em9

GM#11 | C#7b9 | C7b9 | D#7#9 | C7#9

DM7(9) | Bm9 | BbM#11

BbM#11 | B7#9 | B7#9 | Em9

GM#11 | C#7b9 | C7b9 | D#7#9

C7#9 | F7#9 | E7#9 | DM7

Major chords w/ #11 give bichordal fabric and extended color to improvising area:

Ex. GM / FM — OR — #11 of F

FM#11: BbM#11:

Seventh chords w/ #9 allow for modal (gothic-like) flavor...

Ex: Relative Major chord can rest on top

b13 (E7#9b13)

Hints . . . Glimpses (Continued)

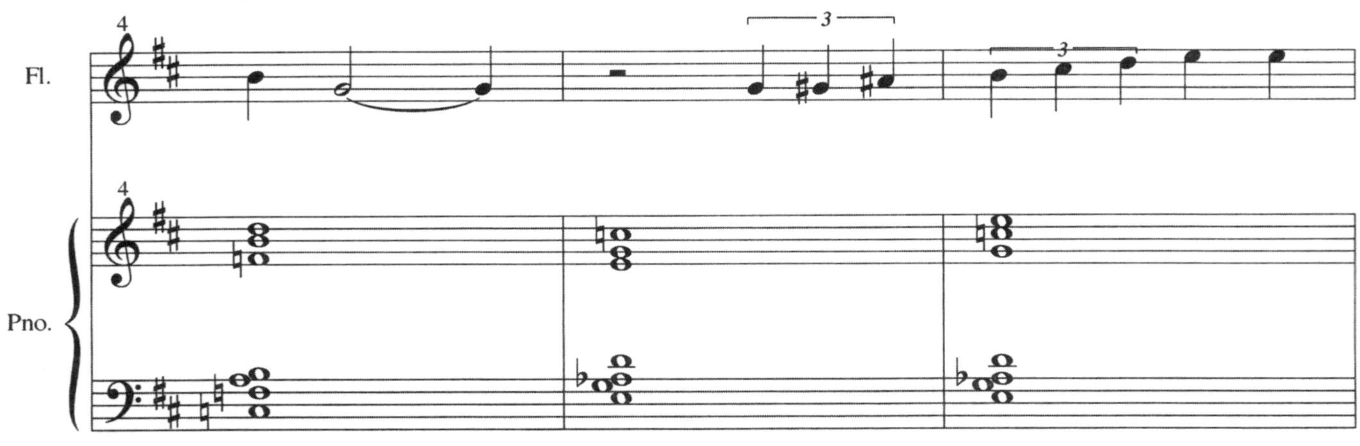

Hints . . . Glimpses (Continued)

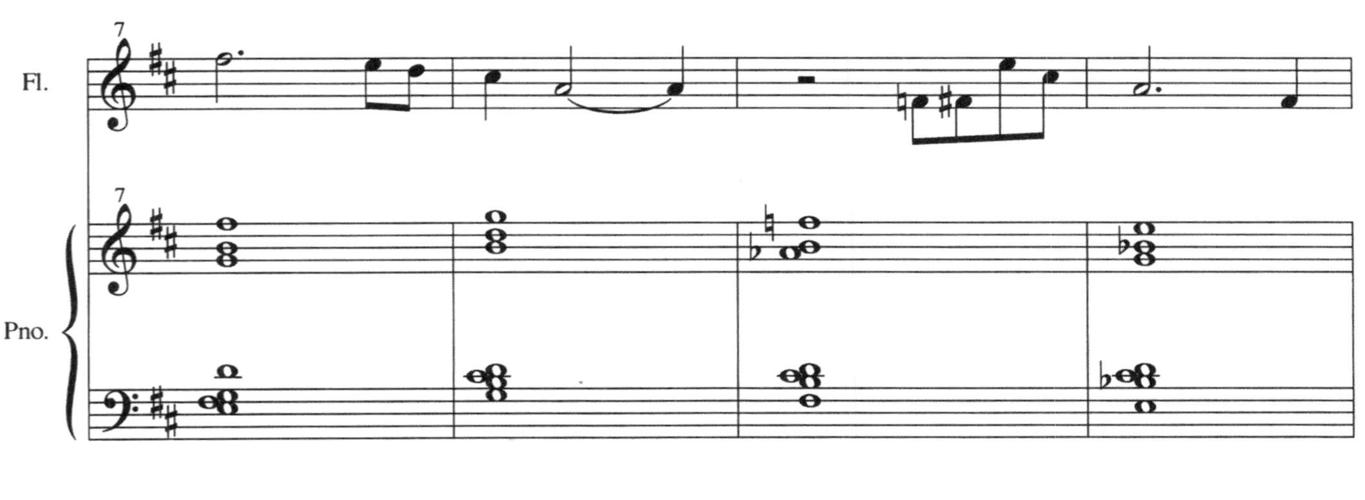

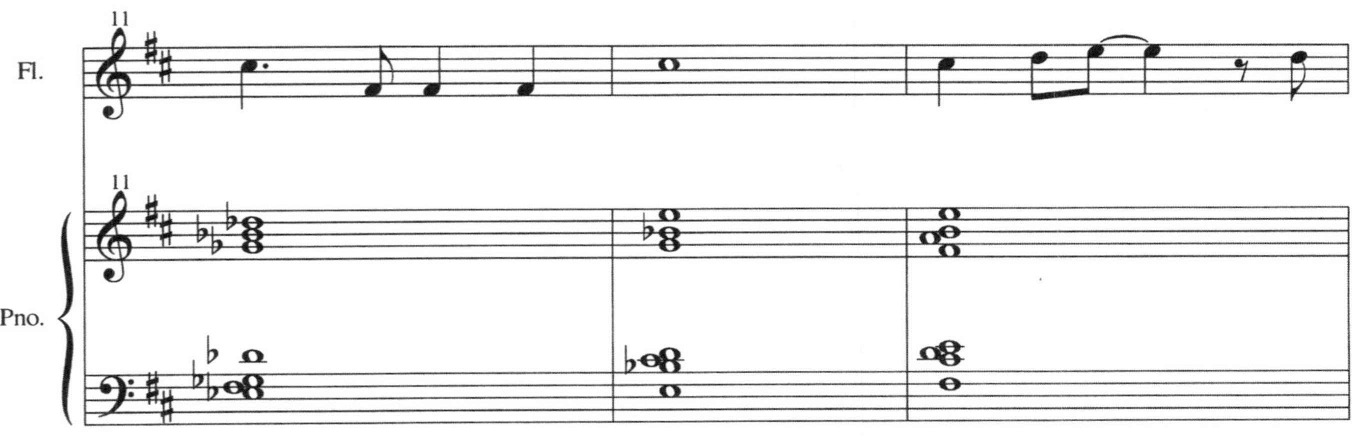

Hints . . . Glimpses (Continued)

Fl.

Pno.

Fl.

Pno.

Fl.

Pno.

Hittin' The Silk

Home Clean

Home Clean (Continued)

I Didn't

~Whimsical~(Infantile)
AM7#11/E
C#13(#11)
D13#9
DM7#11/A
E13
E13#9
D13#9
D13
C#7#9/F
C#7b9
F#m9
B13
DM7
C#7
DM7
C#7
F#7#9
F7#9
1.
E7#9
E13
2.
E7#9
E13
D°(+7)/G#

Ibidem

Inspiration: After Aairam's Letter

Inspiration: After Aairam's Letter (Continued)

Interpenetration: Fresh Air of Majesta

Interpenetration: Fresh Air of Majesta (Continued)

Just In Case You Call

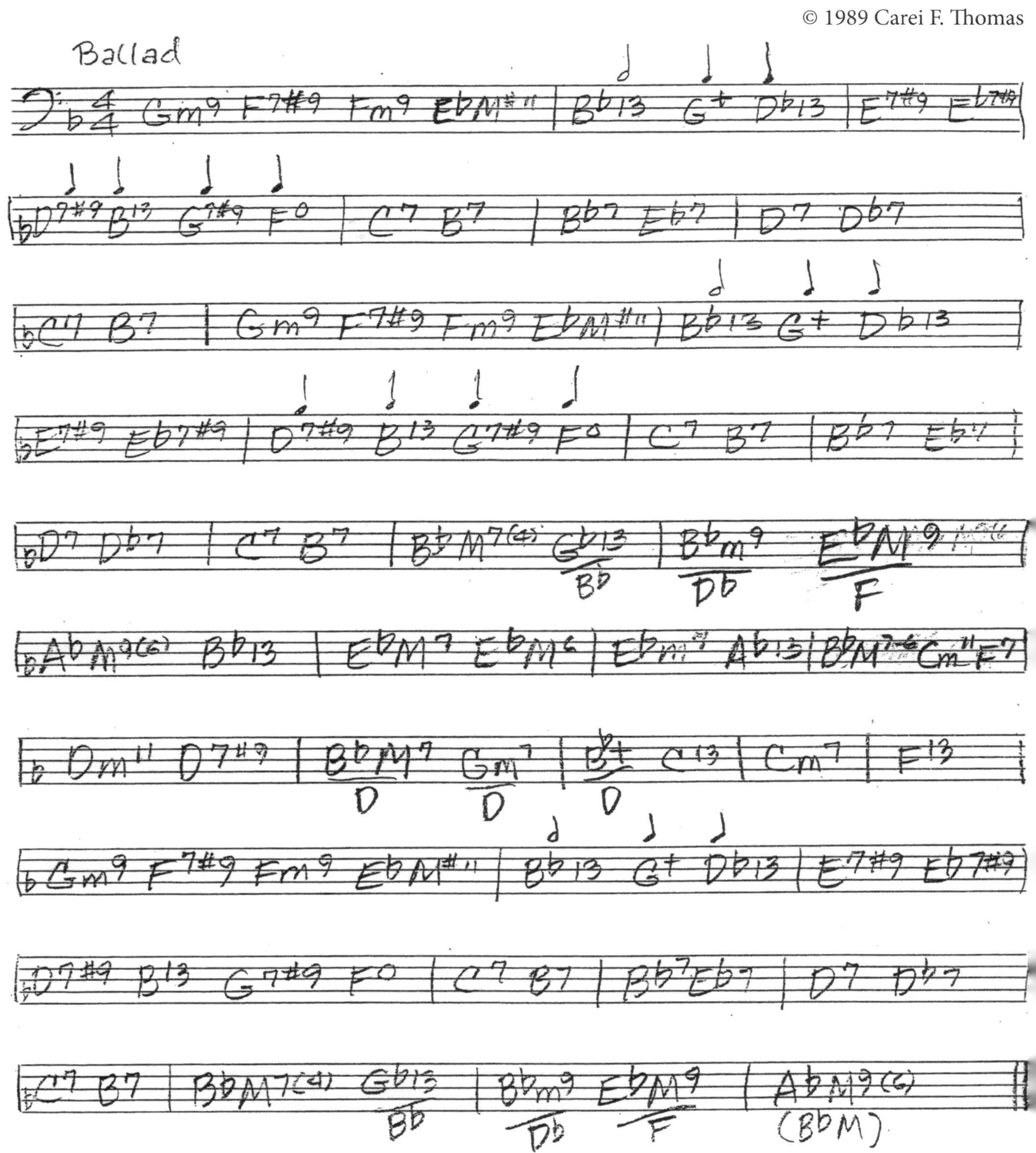

Jy'laahorlx

Jy'laahorlx (Continued)

Jy'laahorlx (Continued)

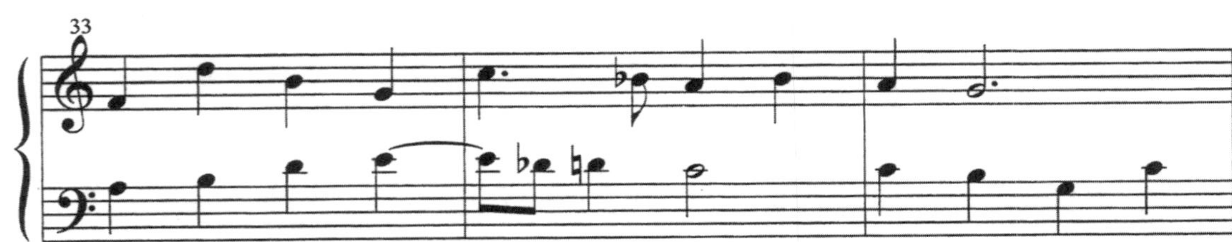

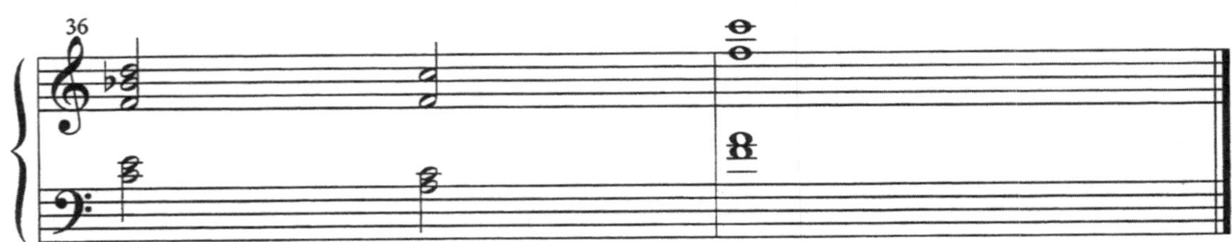

Kansas City Déjà Vu

Kind Ones/Bright Faith

♩≈72

Kwitchurbeliakin

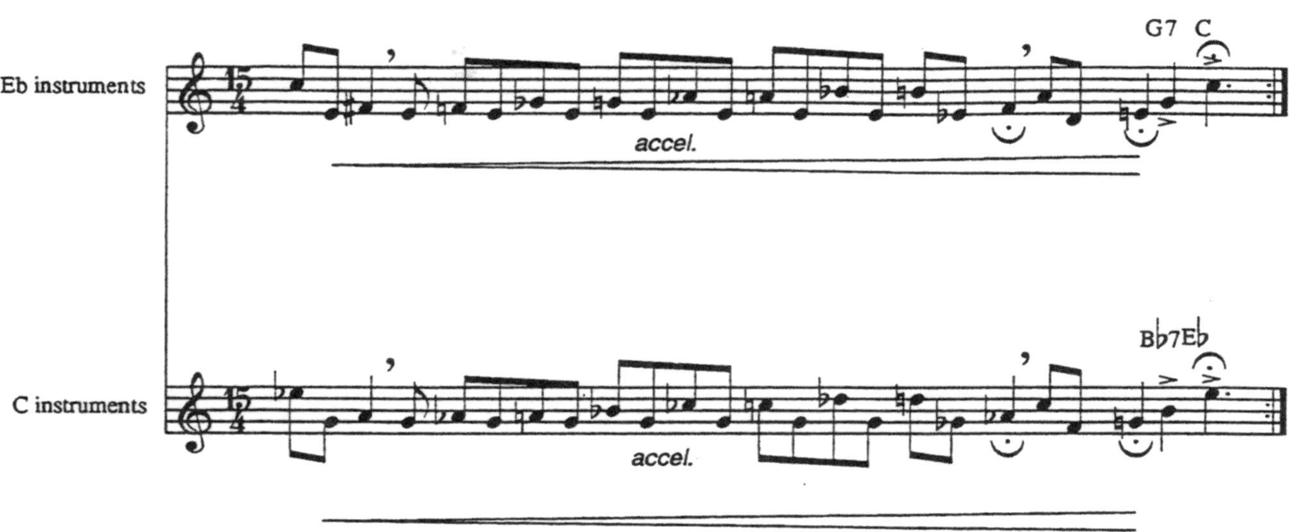

This cartoon was born out of my Triade Improvisational Piano Trio. Cartoons, like my Brief Realities, have written references in them but improvisation is their most important element. Cartoons convey a slapstick, humorous quality and suggest to the instrumentalist(s) to snatch fragments of thematic material and expand it harmonically, temporally, dynamically, and culturally. These are learned the way "doo-wop" singing groups in my inner city neighborhood learned songs—by doing them over and over until, voilá, the piece is born. They can aurally display something 'Cubist' in nature, like the visuals of Braque or Picasso, which give a kind of viscosity to temporal considerations (i.e., accelerando/diminuendo).

Lady Don't Hang Yo' Head Down So Low or Eventually You're Gonna Crack Yo' Spine

Bb instruments

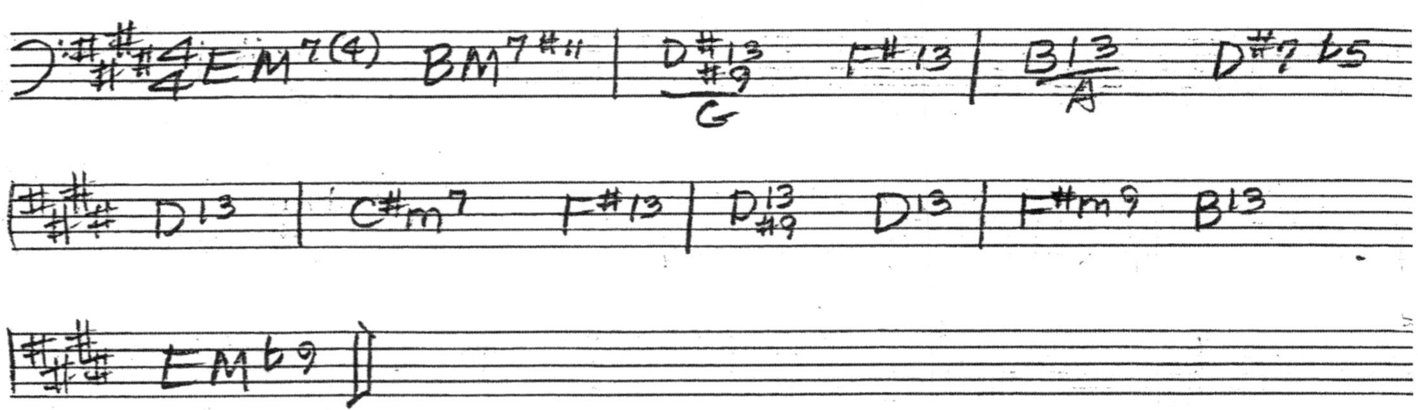

Landing

Landing (Continued)

Lil' Granny's Chariot Come

Look Alikes

Look Alikes (Continued)

9
Fl.
9
Pno.

14
Fl.
14
Pno.

19
Fl.
19
Pno.

Look Alikes (Continued)

Magicmysticmaestromentor

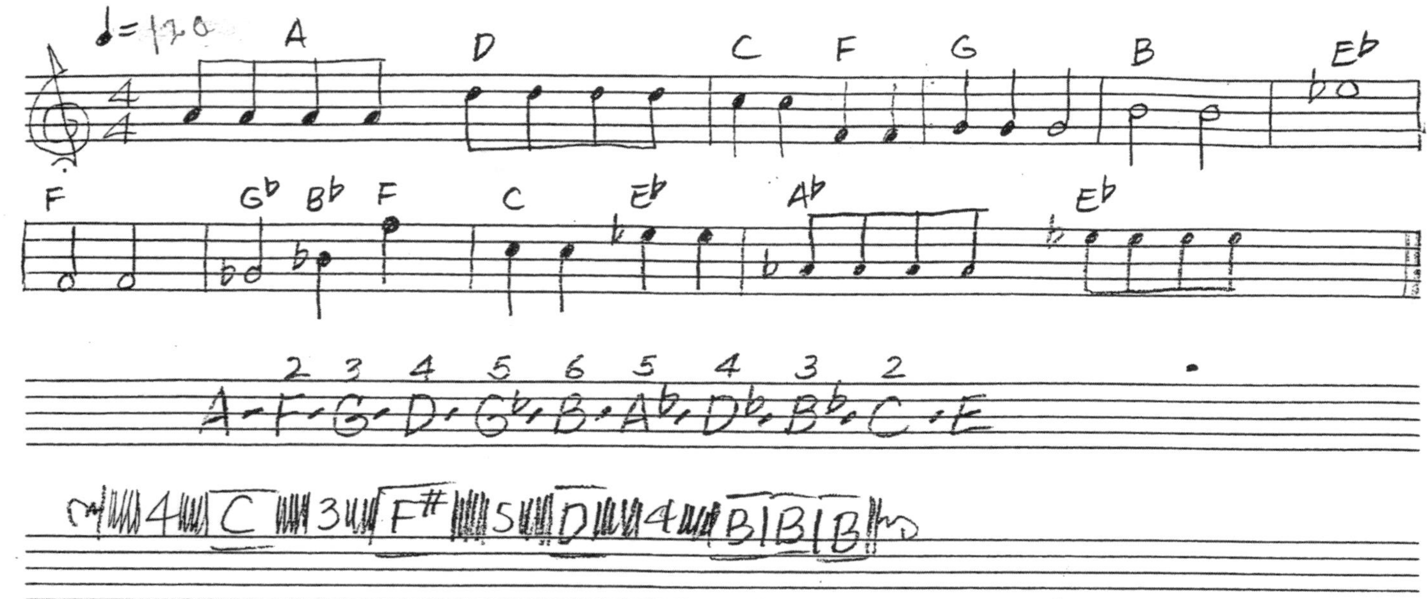

Mary Lou's Chihuly

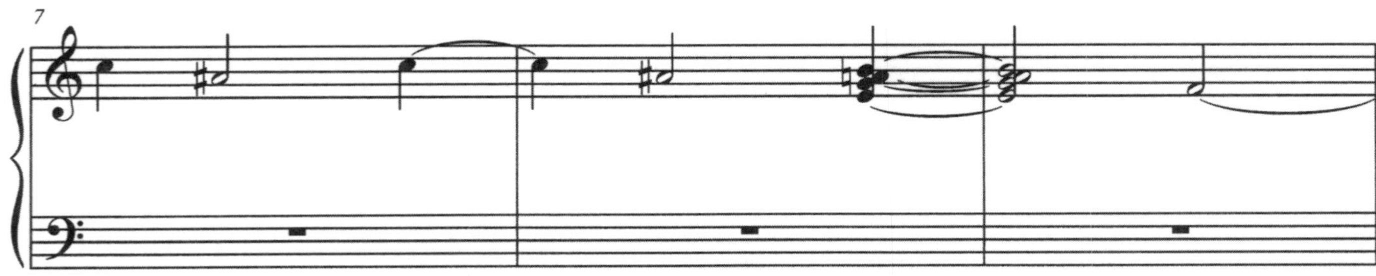

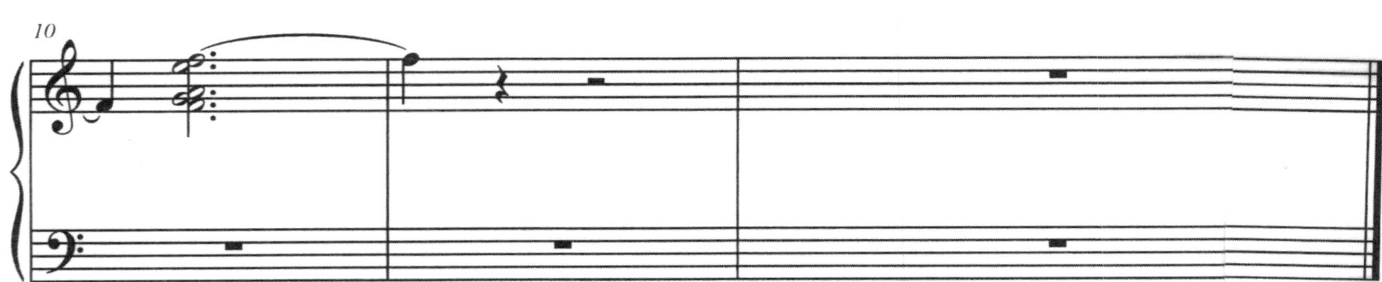

Mary Lou's Chihuly (Continued)

Memory (Dedicated to Frank Nebraska Thomas)

Memory (Dedicated to Frank Nebraska Thomas)
(Continued)

Memory (Dedicated to Frank Nebraska Thomas)
(Continued)

Memory (Dedicated to Frank Thomas)

Minuet for Donna

Mississippi Gentleman Travel'n

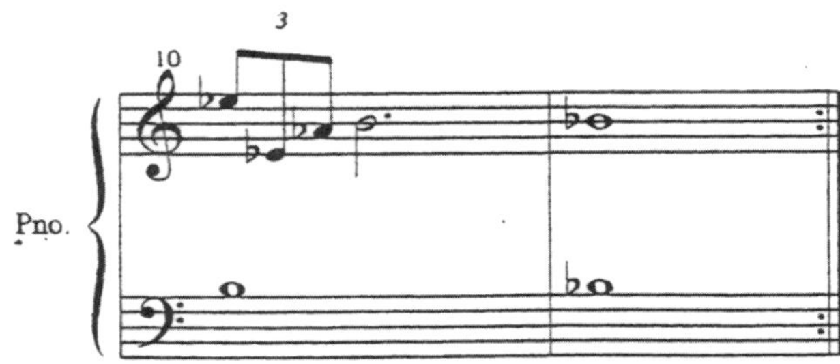

Mom Mary's Troux Bloux Roux

Mom Mary's Troux Bloux Roux (Continued)

Mom Mary's Troux Bloux Roux (Continued)

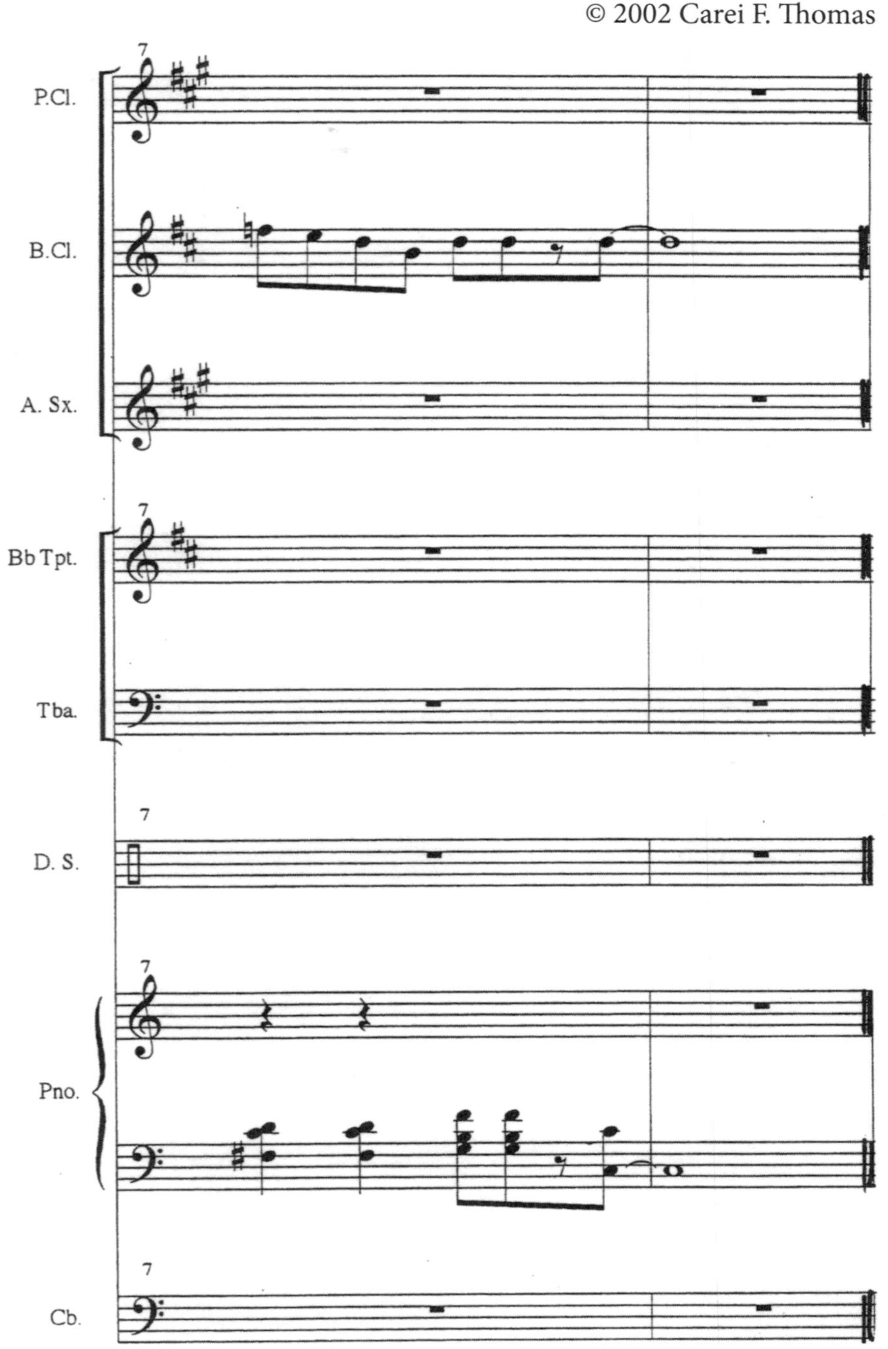

Monsieur Duprée

Arranger

Monsieur Duprée (Continued)

This row is used as an accompaniment. (25 beats – like song.)

(B^b instruments – transposed)

		3	3	2			3	2	4	2	2
F	D	B	G	E	Ab	Db	Gb	Eb	C	A	Bb

The piano uses dominant #9, b13 chords: (concert)

$G^{7\#9}_{b13}$ $E^{7\#9}_{b13}$ $D^{b7\#9}_{b13}$ (3) $A^{7\#9}_{b13}$ (3) $F^{\#7\#9}_{b13}$ (2) $B^{b7\#9}_{b13}$ $E^{b7\#9}_{b13}$ $A^{b7\#9}_{b13}$ (3) $F^{7\#9}_{b13}$ (2)

$D^{7\#9}_{b13}$ (4) $B^{7\#9}_{b13}$ (2) $C^{7\#9}_{b13}$ (2) || ... (25 beats) ...

I wrote this with certain sundry characters in mind I grew up seeing at the picture show at Saturday matinees: Sidney Greenstreet, Charles Laughton, Orson Welles, Victor Buono, Raymond Burr, and, of late, some of the characters portrayed by the portly Marlon Brando and Forrest Whitaker.

A kind of a cartoon noir character study (with cartoonist Gahan Wilson in mind).

My Early 'Trane of Thought

My Early 'Trane of Thought (Continued)

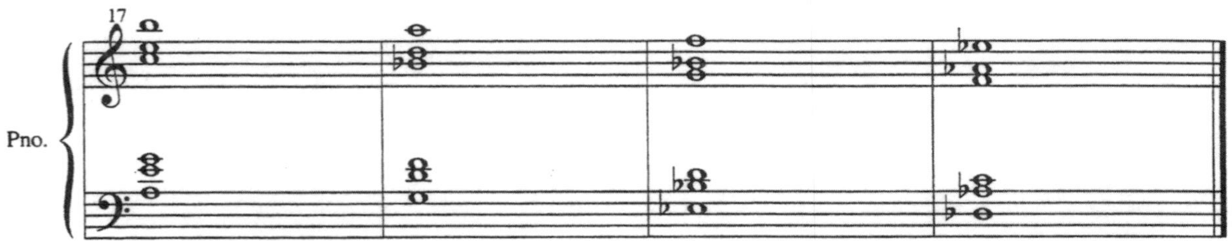

My Early 'Trane of Thought (Handwritten Version)

My Fifth Step During Eclipse

Solennel avec Chaleur

New Same Sweet

No New News Blues/Kohoutek

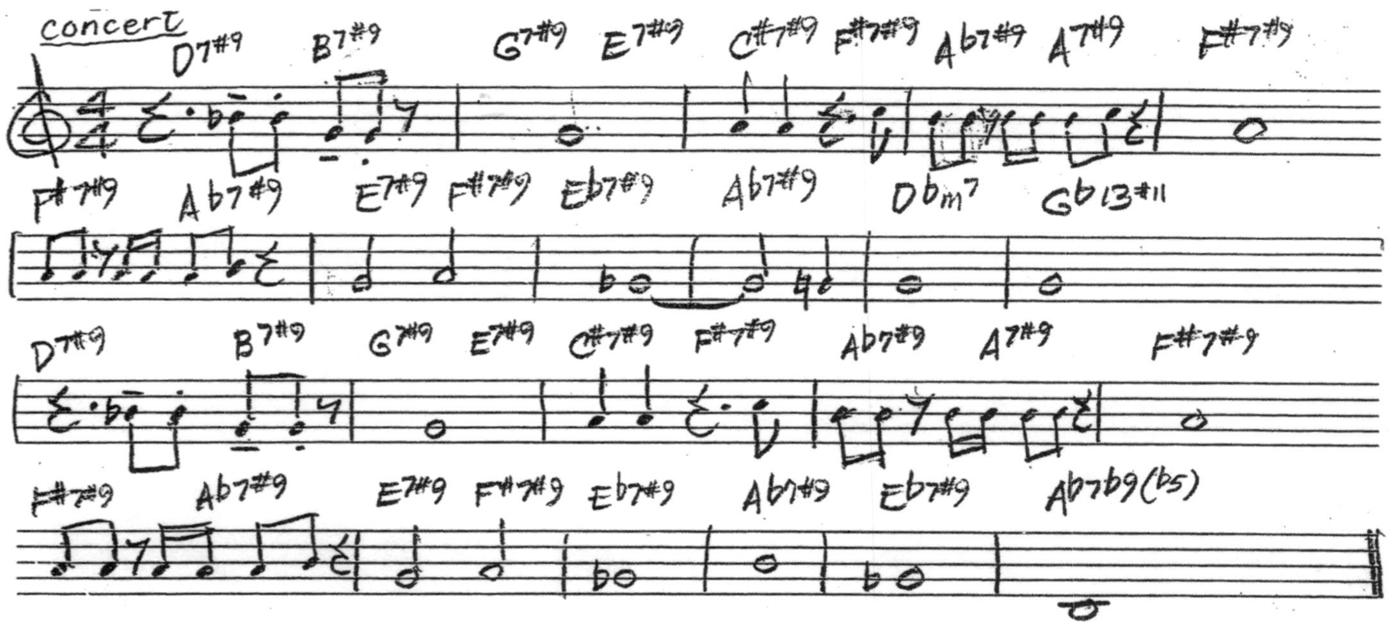

Noir In Purple

(Dedicated to Thelonius Monk, Mal Waldron, and Chopin)

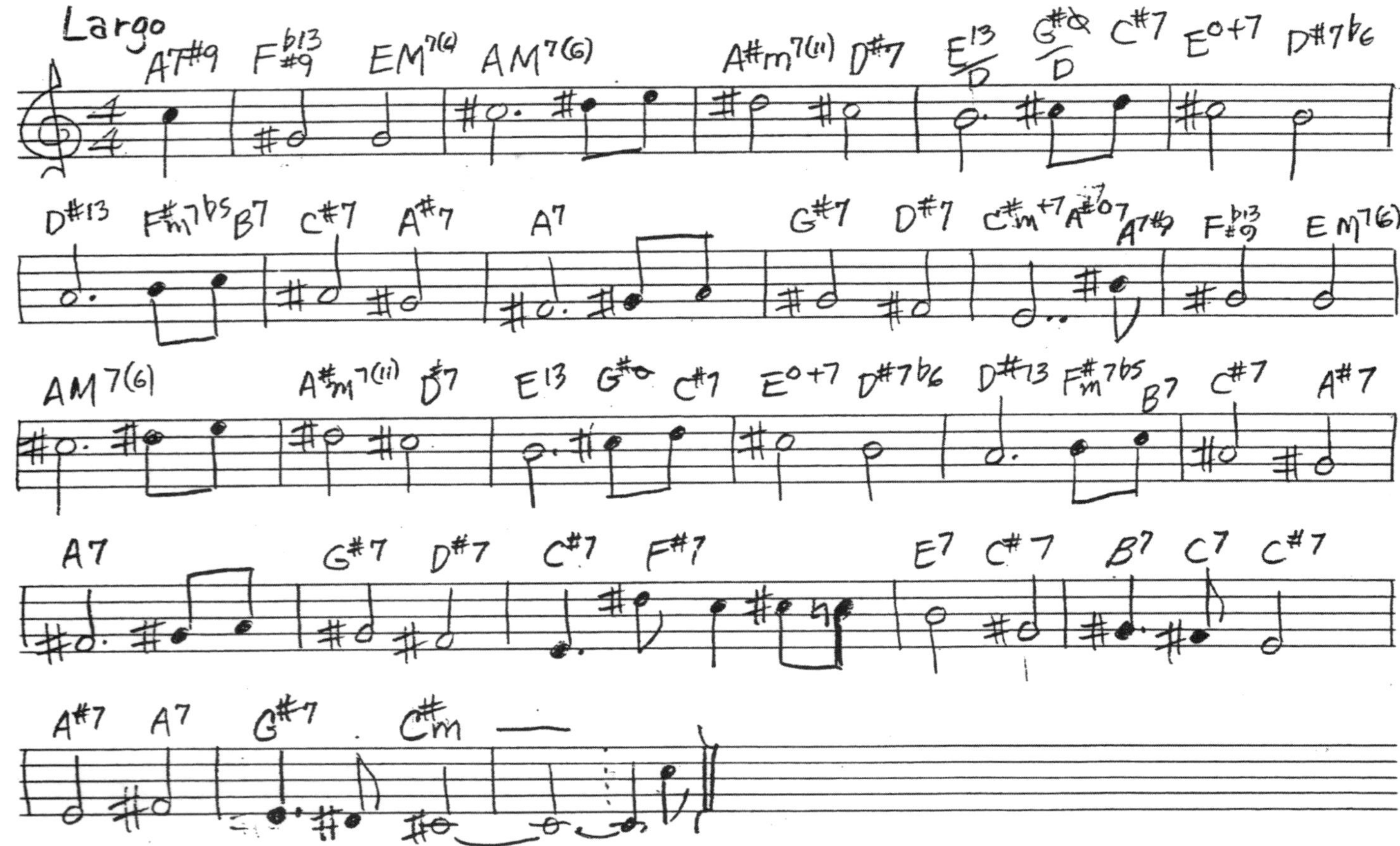

Nothing Personal

Nys

Concert pitch
Am11
F♯m11
Em11
C13
Bm11
Am11
Bm11
F♯7♯9
C13
Bm11
Am11
Bm11
F♯7♯9
C13

Of Families and Friends

Of Times Old and New

One Final Answer: Photochromokinesis IV

One Final Answer: Photochromokinesis IV
(Continued)

One Final Answer: Photochromokinesis IV
(Continued)

One Final Answer: Photochromokinesis IV
(Continued)

One Final Answer: Photochromokinesis IV
(Continued)

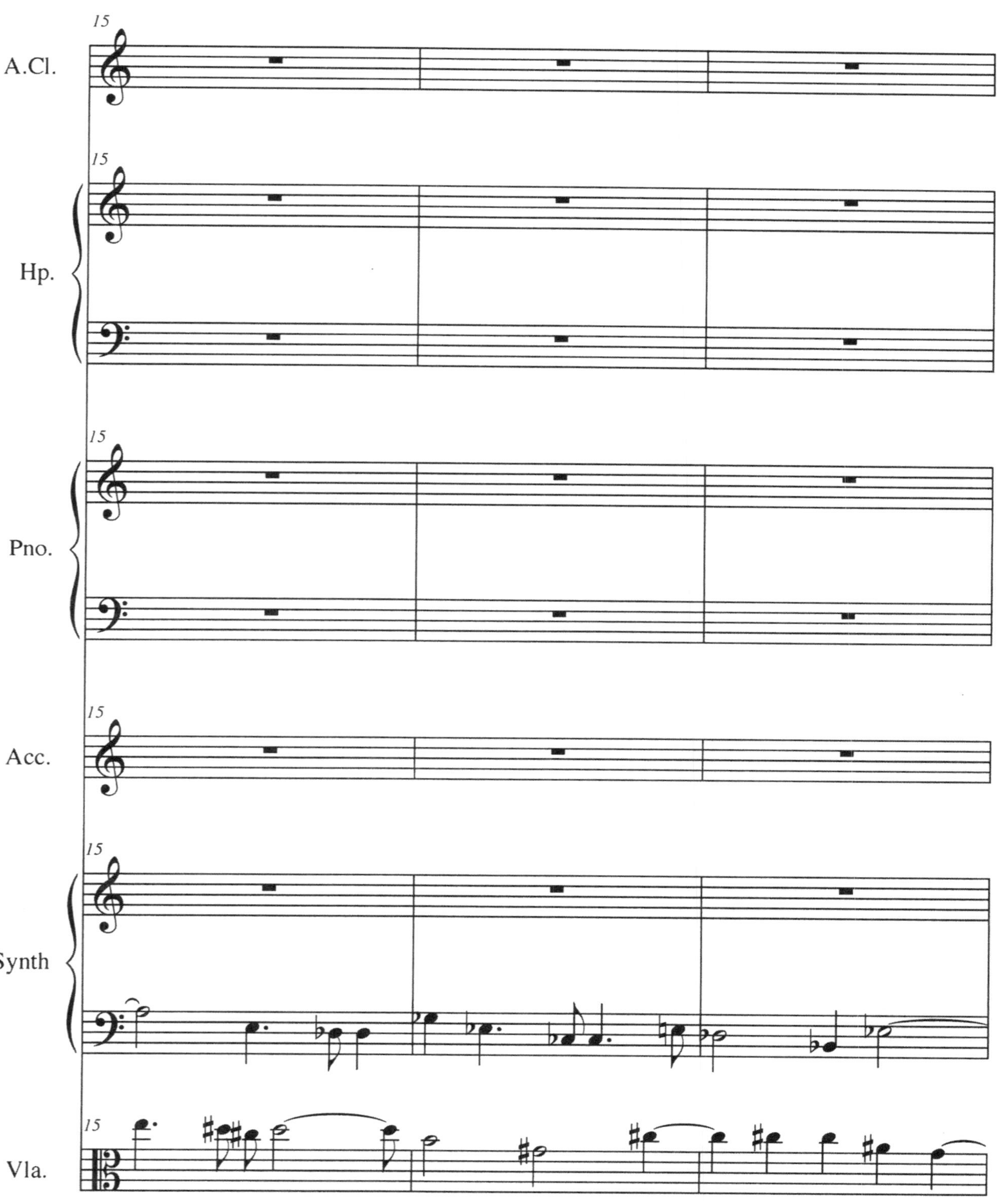

One Final Answer: Photochromokinesis IV
(Continued)

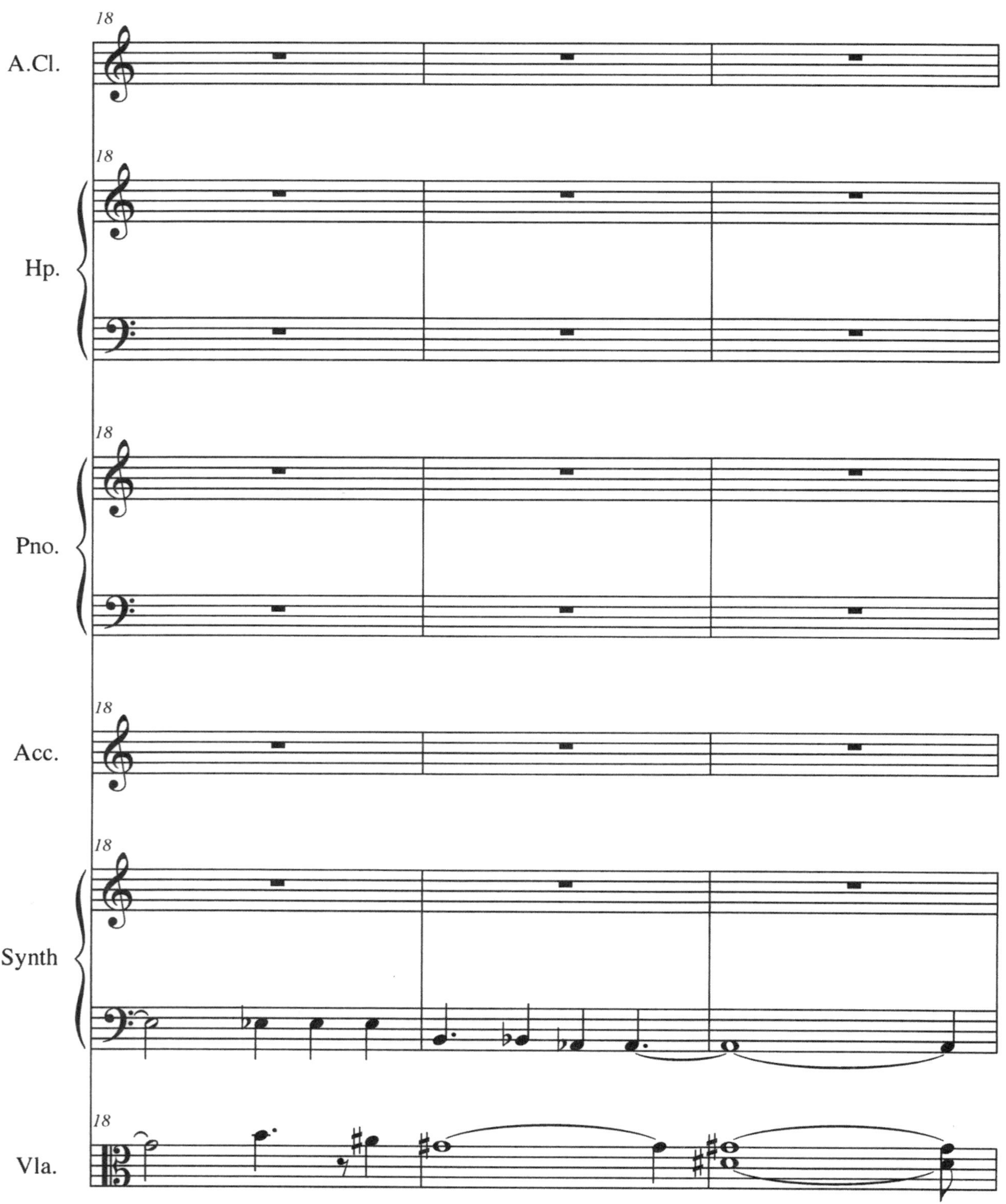

One Final Answer: Photochromokinesis IV
(Continued)

One Final Answer: Photochromokinesis IV
(Continued)

One Final Answer: Photochromokinesis IV
(Continued)

One Final Answer: Photochromokinesis IV
(Continued)

One Final Answer: Photochromokinesis IV
(Continued)

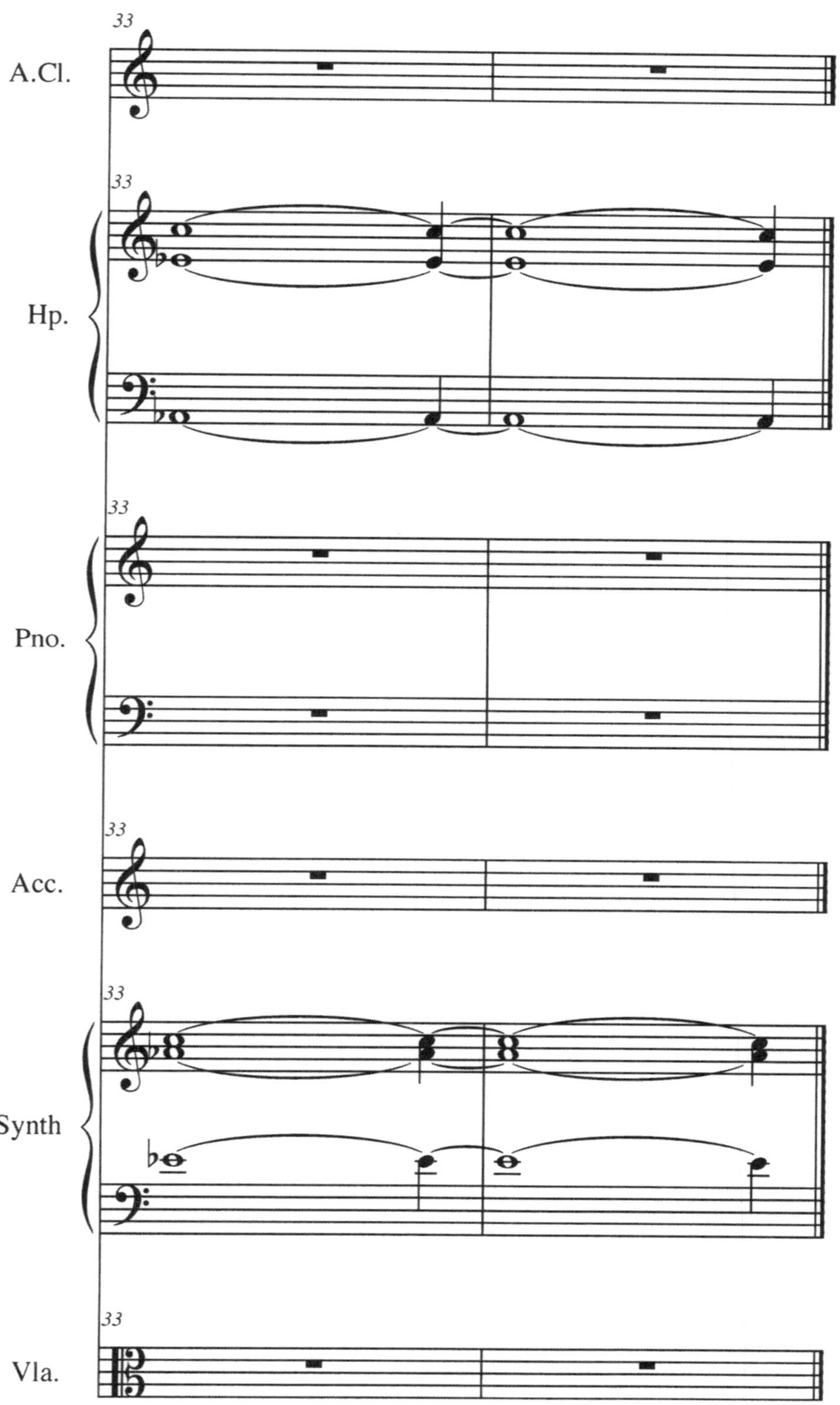

One True Essence of Grümbelmüüch

One True Essence of Grümbelmüüch (Continued)

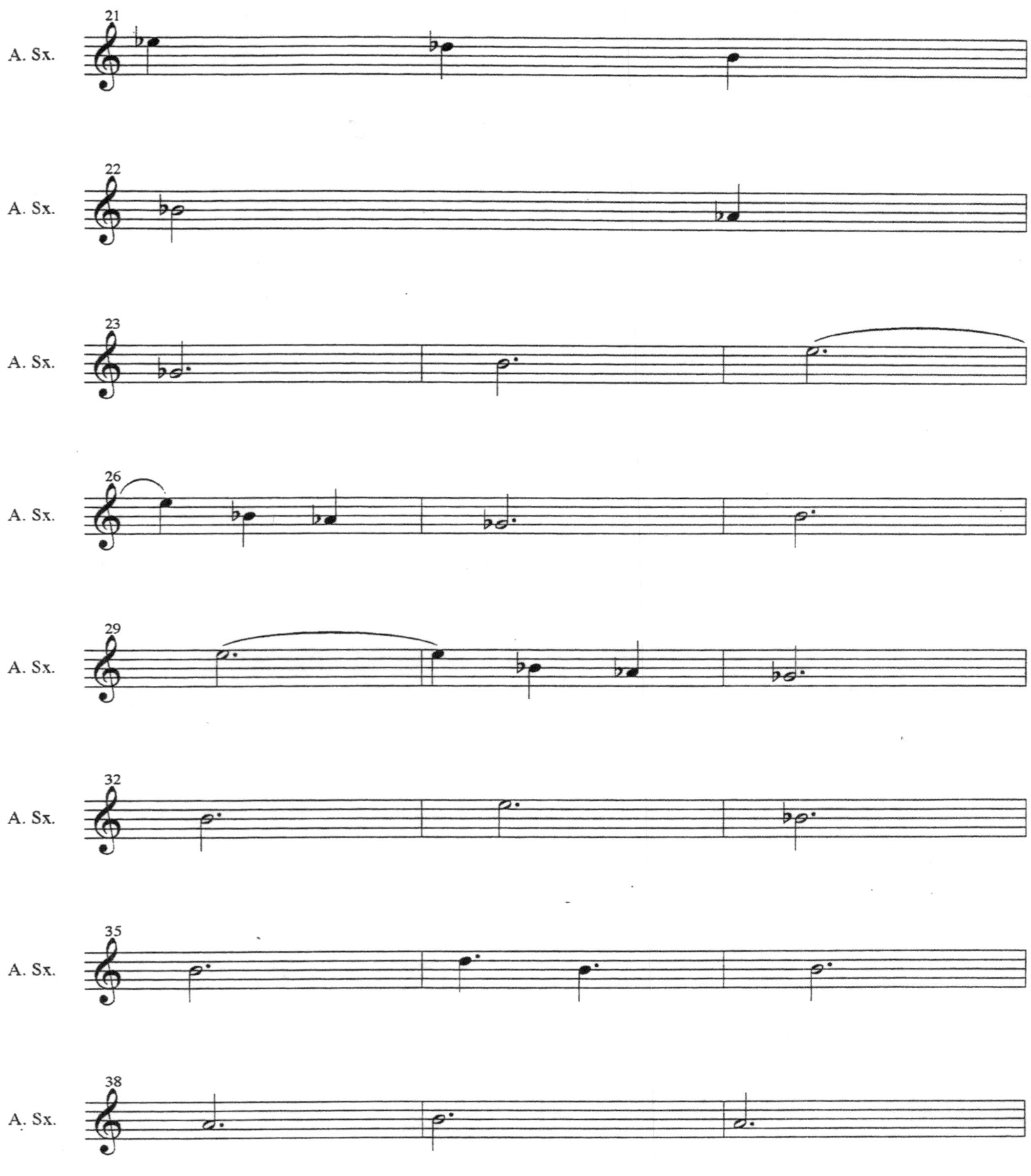

One True Essence of Grümbelmüüch (Continued)

Opalessence/Chiron

Our Tryst Waltz

Our Tryst Waltz (Continued)

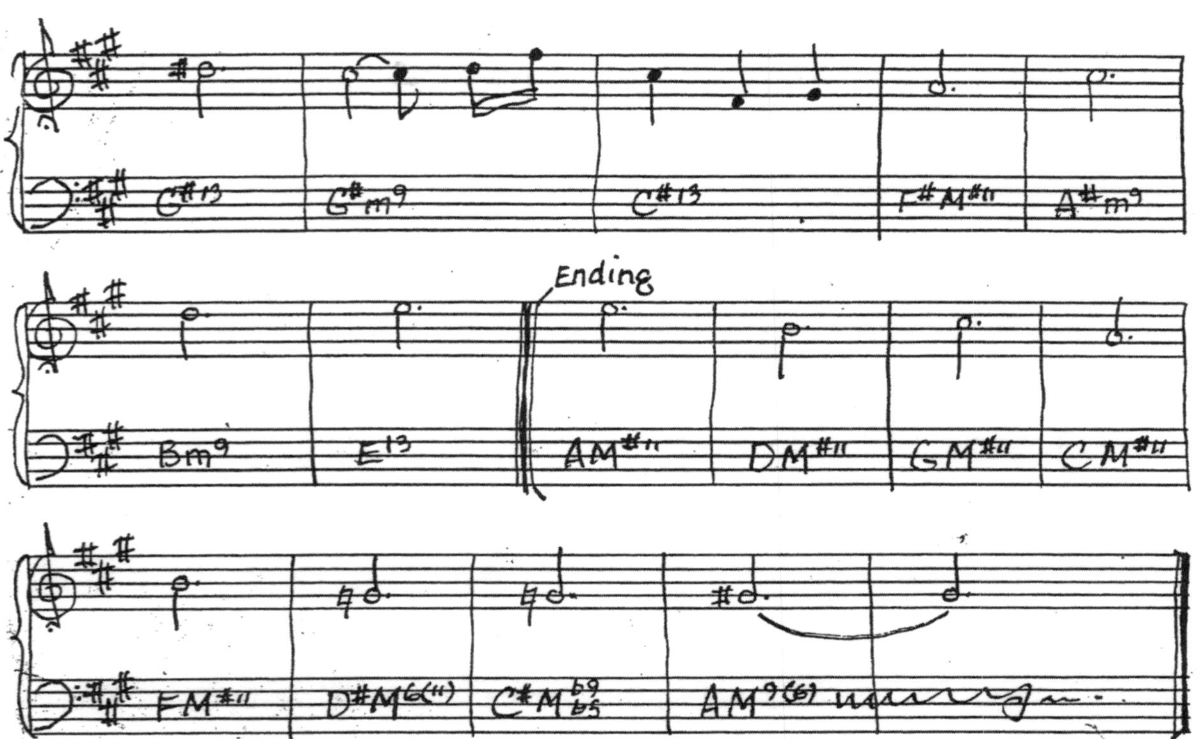

Pat's Place Saturdays

© 1966 Carei F. Thomas

Precious Waltz

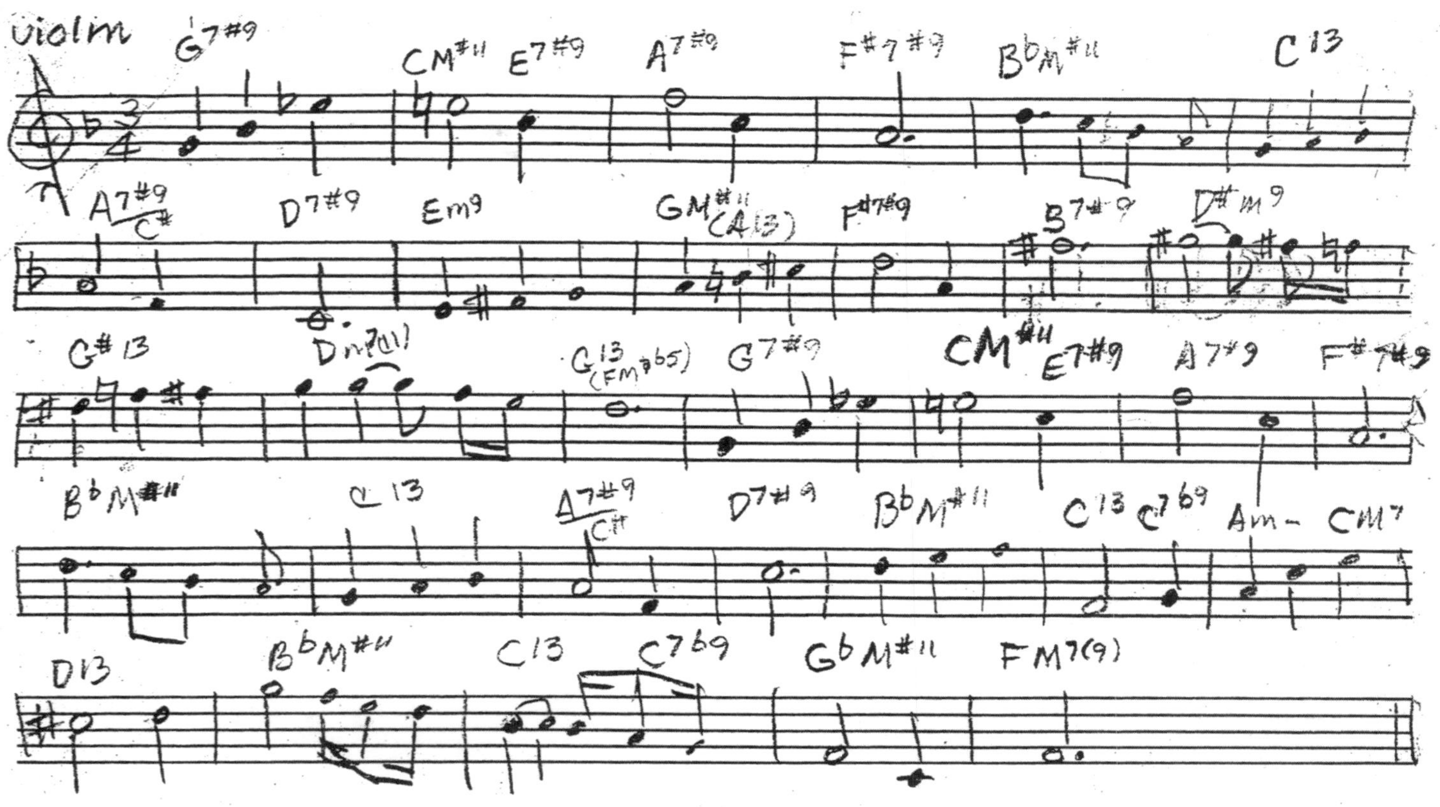

Quesyi

concert pitch

Quiet By Now

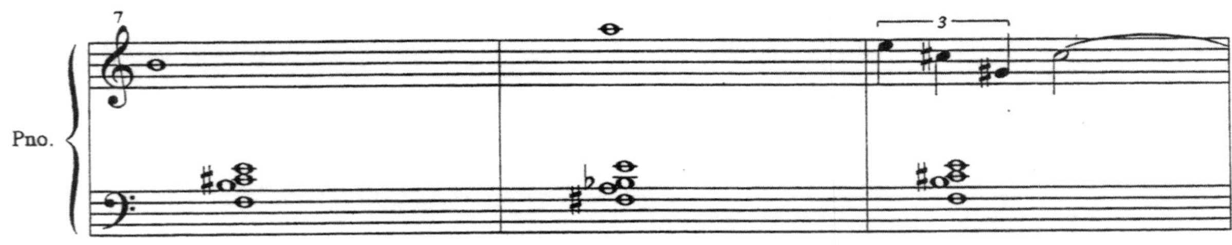

Quiet By Now (Continued)

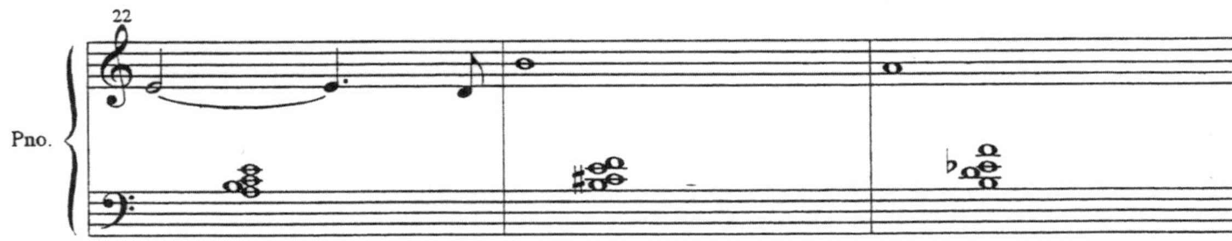

Quiet By Now (Continued)

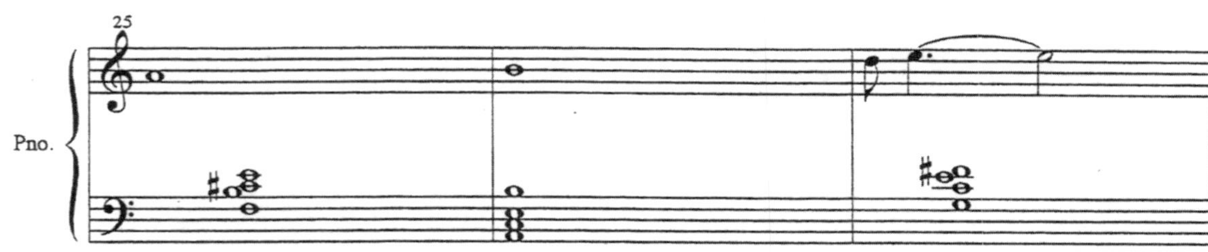

Quippihd

Soprano Saxophone
Piano
A7#9 b13
D7#9 b13
C#7#9 b13
B7#9 b13
A7#9 b13
E7#9 b13
4
S. Sx.
Pno.
C#7#9 b13 (AM)
A7#9 b13
D7#9 b13
AM(4) GM(4) FM(4)

Quippihd (Continued)

Rhyssaal

Rhyssaal (Continued)

4

Bb Cl.

3

4

Bb Tpt.

4

Gtr.

4

Pno.

4

Cb.

Rhyssaal (Continued)

Roagjyii-Ahl

Robert Fitzgerald/Home Early

Sentempathy

Sh-h-h! This is the Best Part

Sh-h-h! This is the Best Part (Continued)

Sh-h-h! This is the Best Part

BASS

3 [BM / Eb7#9] ~ [FM / A7#9] ~ 3 [AM / C#7#9] ~ 2 [BbM / D7#9] ~ [EbM / G7#9] ~ 2 [GM / B7#9]

[DbM / F7#9] ~ 2 [AbM / C7#9] ~ [DM / F#7#9] ~ 3 [BbM / D7#9] ~ 2 [CM / E7#9] ~ 4 [AbM / C7#9]

7 [PRISM / FM(4) / (sus) c] ~ [AM / C#7#9] ~ [GM / B7#9] ~ [AbM / C7#9] ~ [BbM / D7#9] ~ 3 [PRISM / CM(4) / (sus) c]

[CM / E7#9] ~ 3 [AM / C#7#9] ~ [(BM) / Bb7#9] ~ 4 [BbM / D7#9] ~ 3 [AM / C#7#9] ~ 2 [DbM / F7#9]

[EbM / G7#9] ~ 3 [FM / A7#9] ~ [GbM / Bb7#9] ~ [GM / B7#9] ||

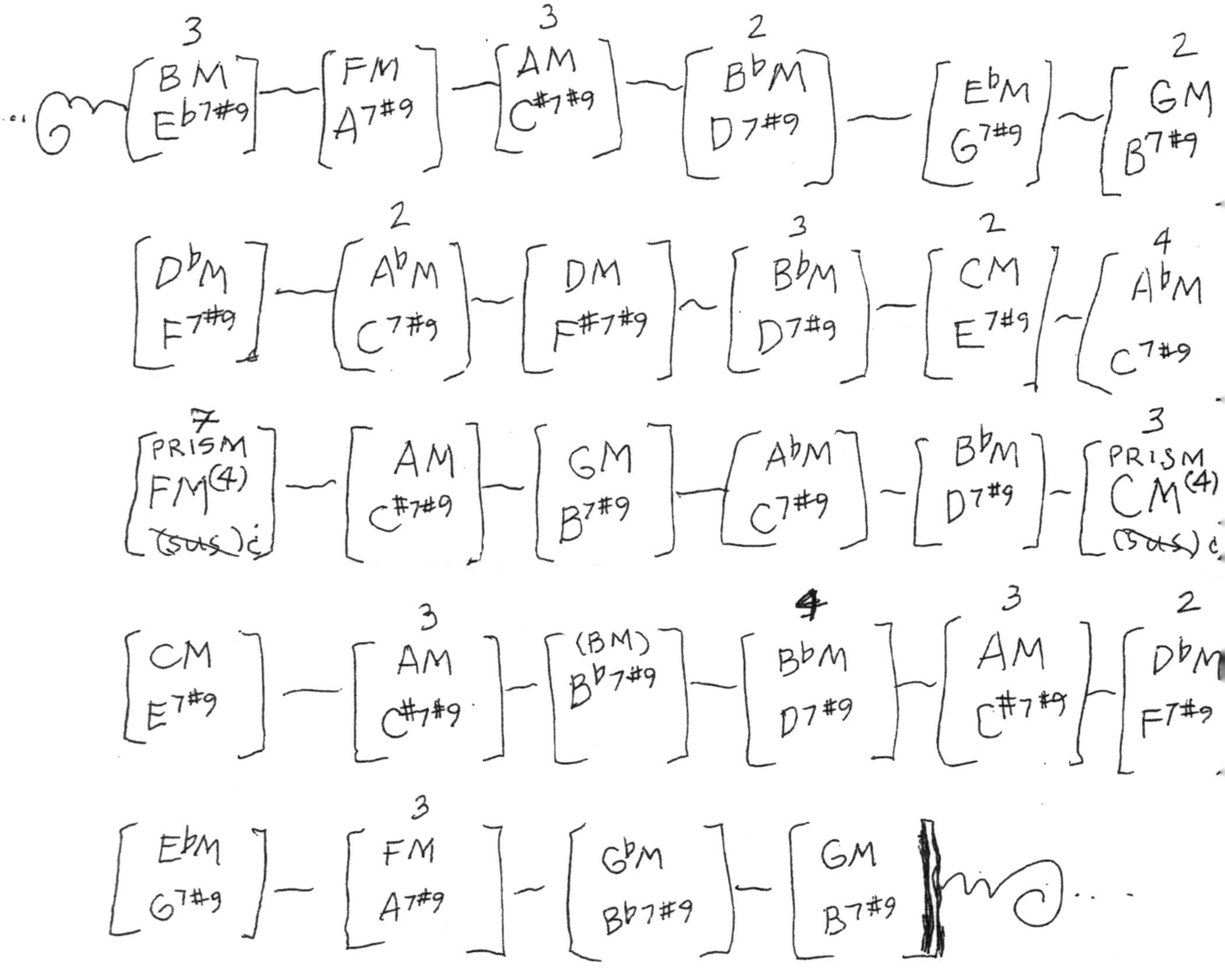

notice:

You can start on any one of these, once you've done the original row: [Eb7#9 to B7#9]. Just try to complete row sequence

Simile I

Clarinet in Bb
Bass Clarinet
Piano
Contrabass
B♭7
B♭7
3
Bb Cl.
B.Cl.
Pno.
Cb.
CM (Em)
CM
Fm6
B♭M (Dm)

Simile I (Continued)

Sir Martin of Upton Heights

Sir Martin of Upton Heights (Continued)

Sir Martin of Upton Heights (Continued)

Sir Martin of Upton Heights (Continued)

Sir Martin of Upton Heights (Continued)

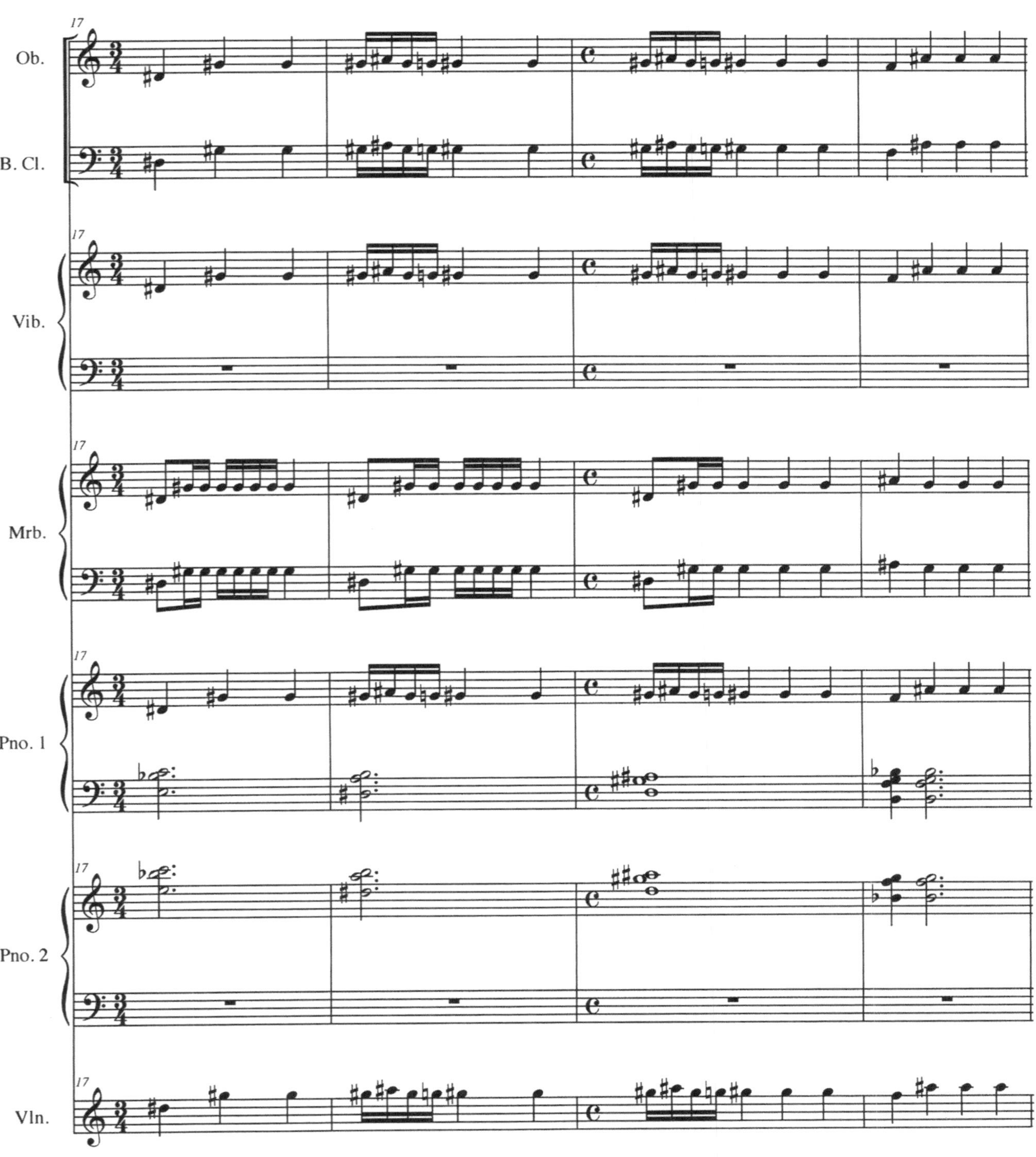

Sir Martin of Upton Heights (Continued)

21

Ob.

B. Cl.

Vib.

Mrb.

Pno. 1

Pno. 2

Vln.

Sky

concert
A♭m11
Em9
CM7
D♭m11
Cm7
Bm9
Dm11
Fm11
GM9(6)
Em9
=10 beats
COLOR ROW
E♭–D♭–B–G♭–A♭–B♭–G–A–D–C–F
=22
B♭–G–E♭–C–A–F–D–C♭–B–E–D♭
=22
C–F–B♭–E♭–A♭–D♭–G♭–B–E–A–D–G–E
D
(See Extensions in Ruminations Section)

Slymn Hymn

Flute
Alto Saxophone
Tenor Saxophone
Trumpet in Bb
Fl.
A. Sx.
T. Sx.
Bb Tpt.
4

Slymn Hymn (Continued)

Slymn Hymn (Continued)

15

Fl.

A. Sx.

T. Sx.

15

Bb Tpt.

Em11 F#7#9 b5 G7#9 CM9(#11) 13 BbM#11 ⁒ ⁒ ⁒ ⁒

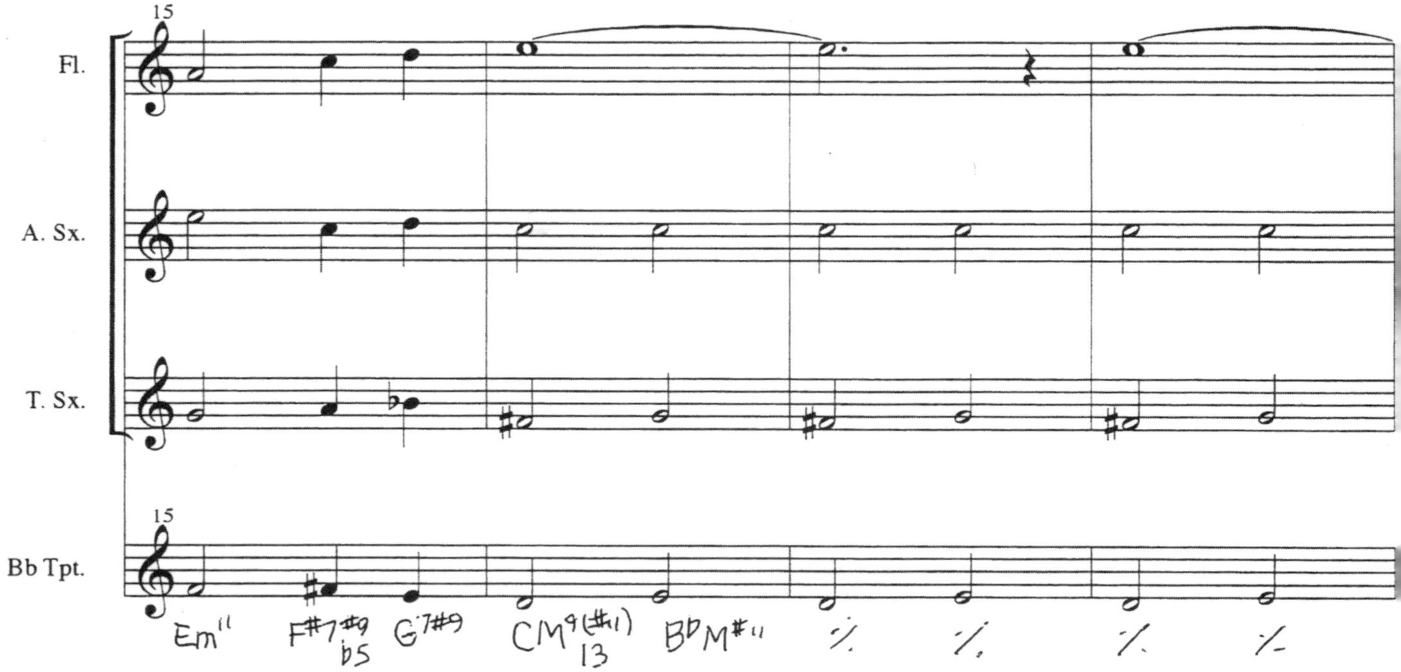

Spanky

Spanky (Continued)

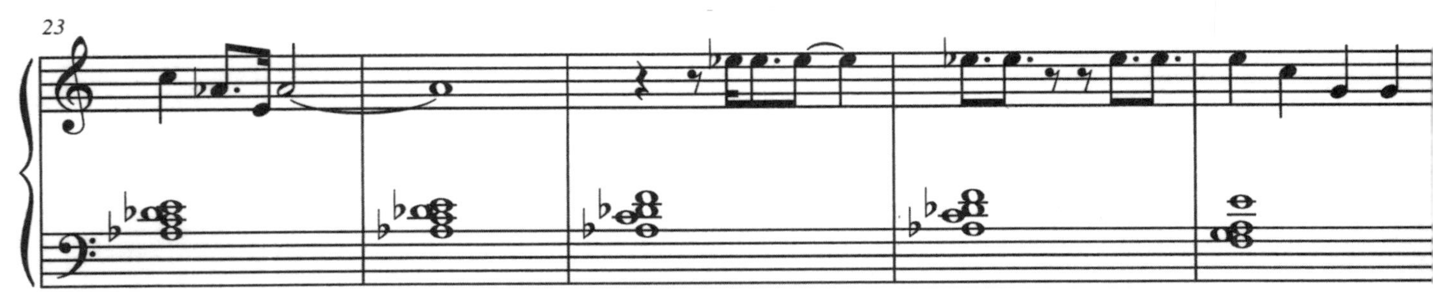

Steps

Alto Saxophone
Tenor Saxophone
Trumpet in Bb
Drum Set
Piano
Contrabass

Steps (Continued)

Steps (Continued)

Steps (Continued)

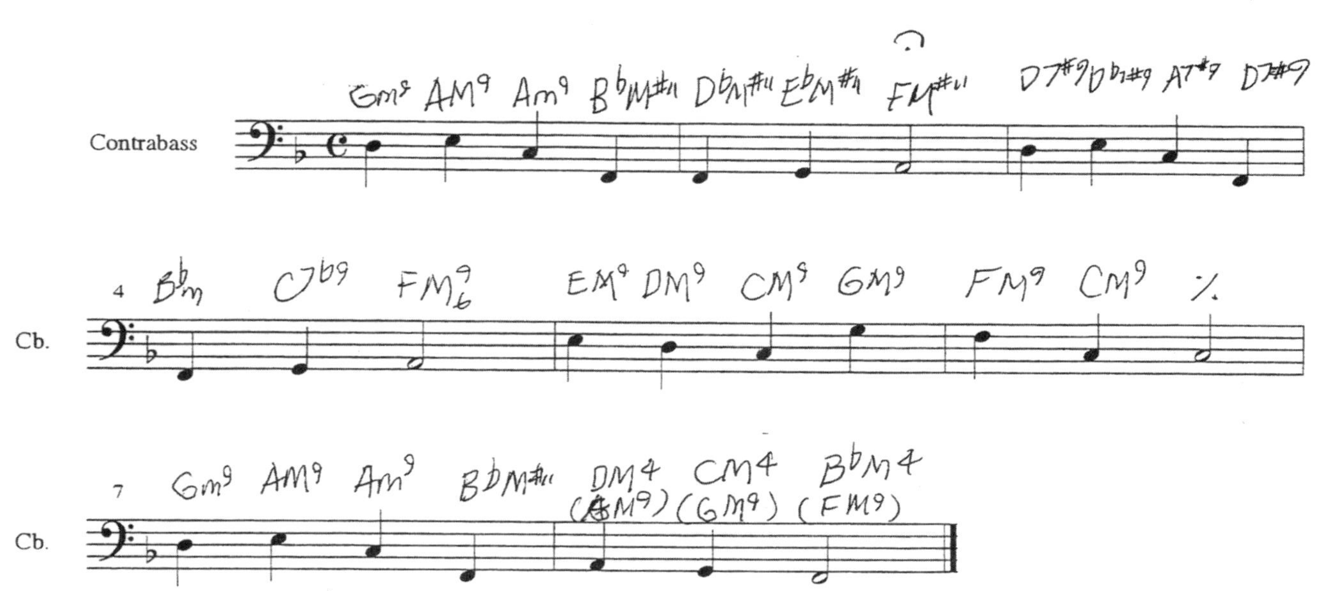

Still Time

GM9 GM#11 F#7b13 CM#11
EM7(9) C#m9 Bbm9(11) Eb13 F#m9 B13
Eb7b9 Ab7#9 b13 Db7#9 b13 Fm7(9) Bb13 Bbm9 Dbo+7 (Eb7b9)
GM9 GM#11 F#7#9 b13 CM#11
EM7(9) C#m9 Bbm9(11) Eb13 F#m9 B13
Abm7(9) Db13 Bo+7 (Db7b9) F#m9 B13 Ao+7 (B7b9)
Em7(9) A13 Go+7 (A7b9) Dm11 G13 F#o+7 (Ab7b9)
CM#11 D13 Bm9 Am9 F#m9 EM9

Still Time (Continued)

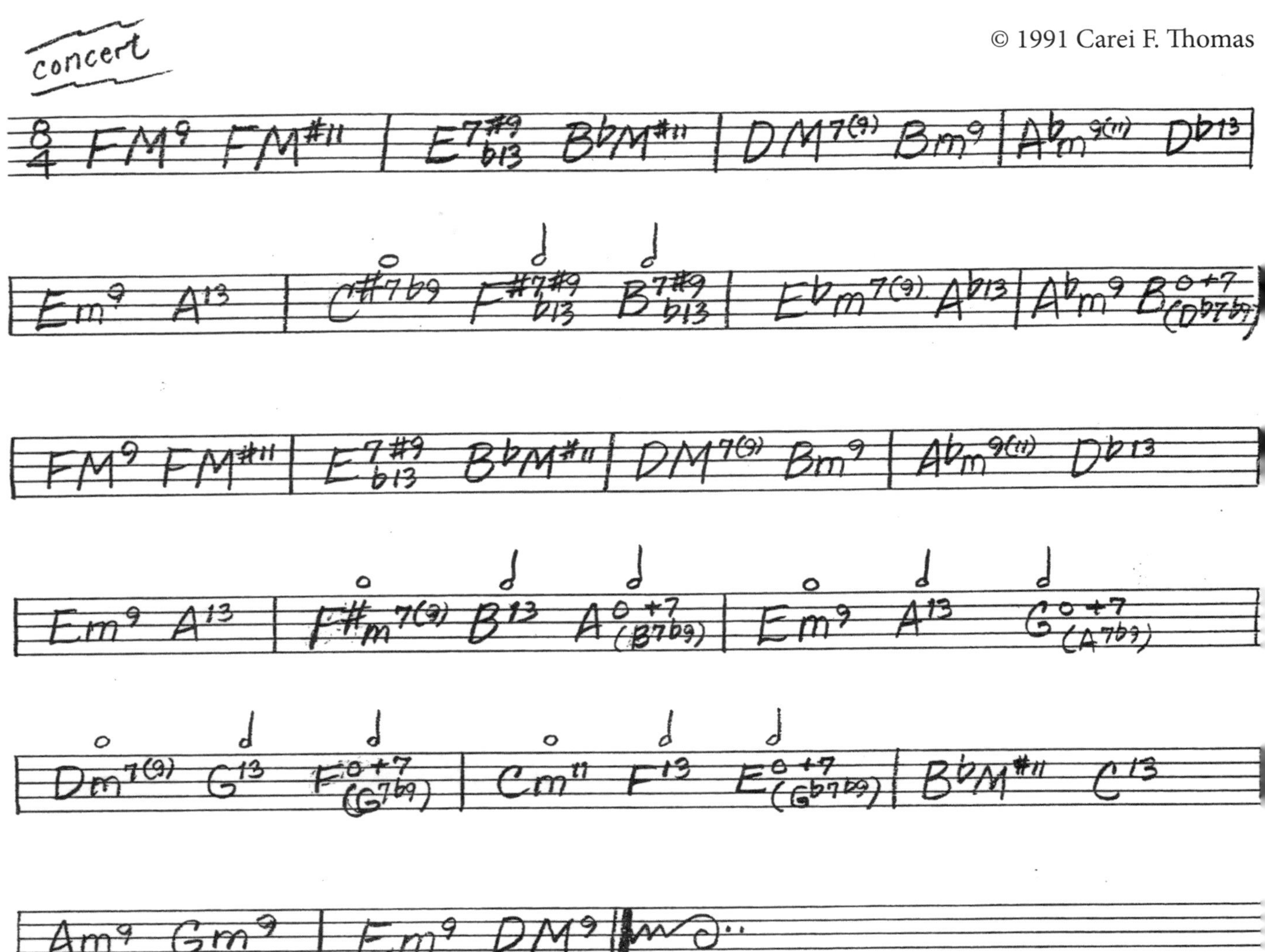

Story Line: Everyone's On Their Way Home

Swe' Potatah: An Old Jazz Song for Bennie and Wayne

Synescalatoria

Piano

Thank You Mother, Thank You Father

The Boys, Jaahri and Aairam

Another cartoon depicting "the boys," my sons—Jaahred Careim and Aairam Cjalme—at play some years ago. Notice the skin of the piece is in 5/4. Whatever!

The Boys, Jaahri and Aairam

The Boys, Jaahri and Aairam (Continued)

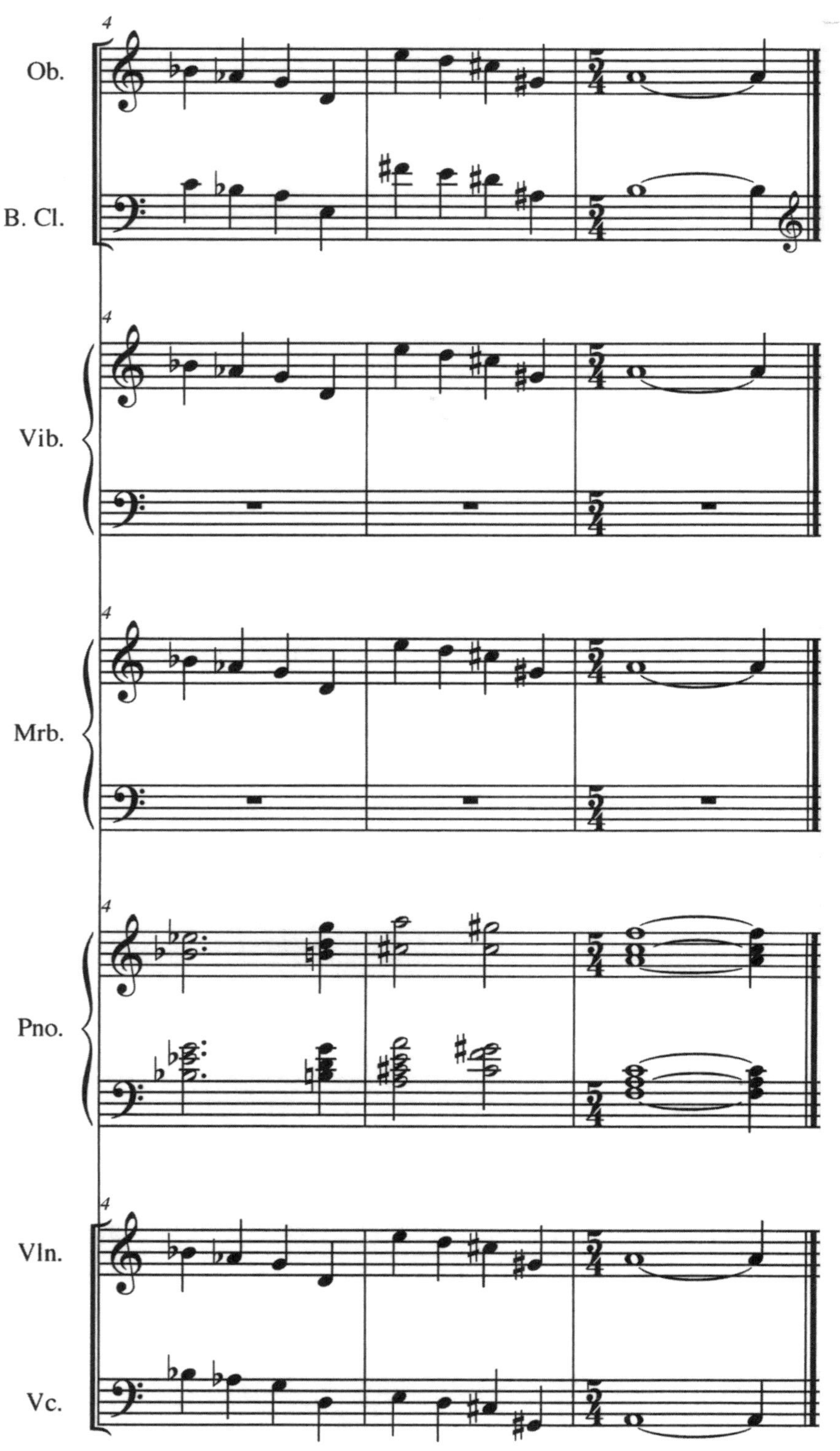

The Girls at Gröensbürgwalstraat 27

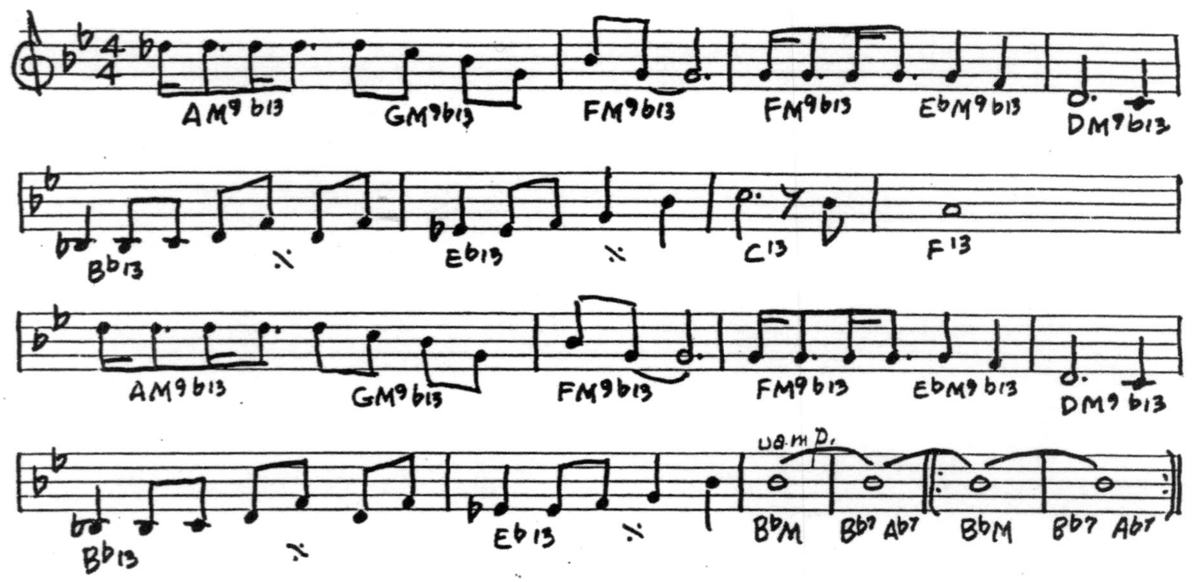

Concert

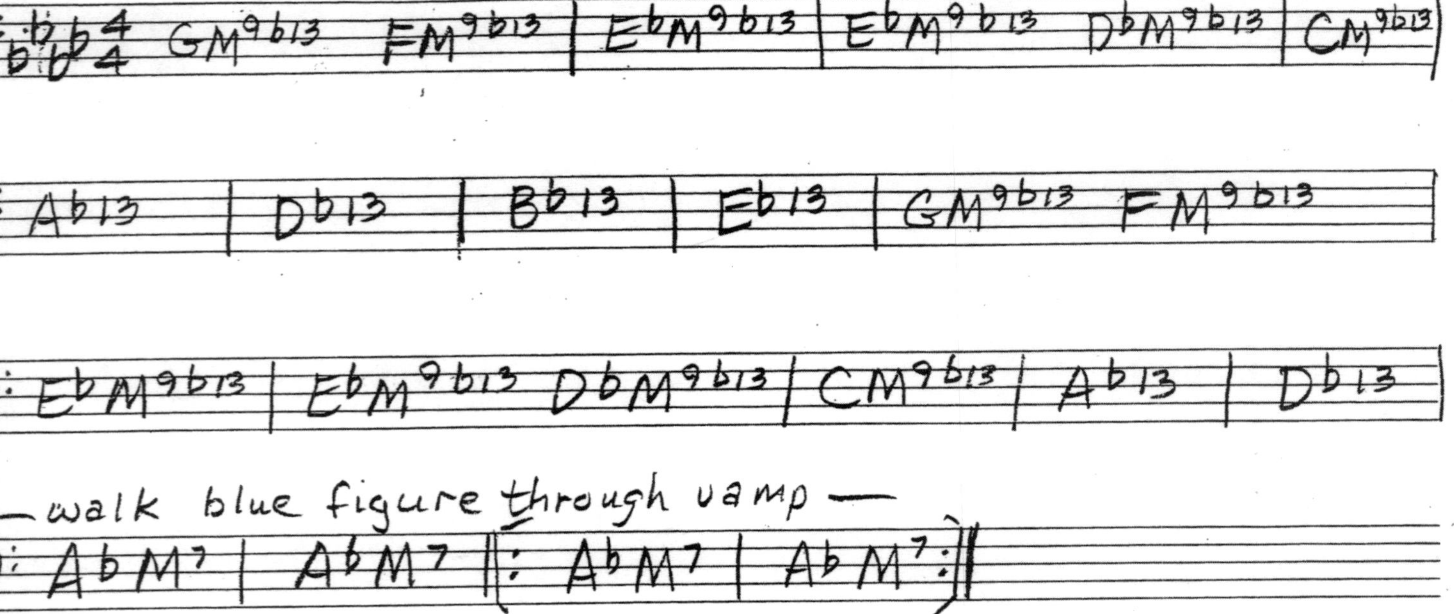

The Valentine's Day

The Valley, The Shadow and The Light

There, Off Yonder

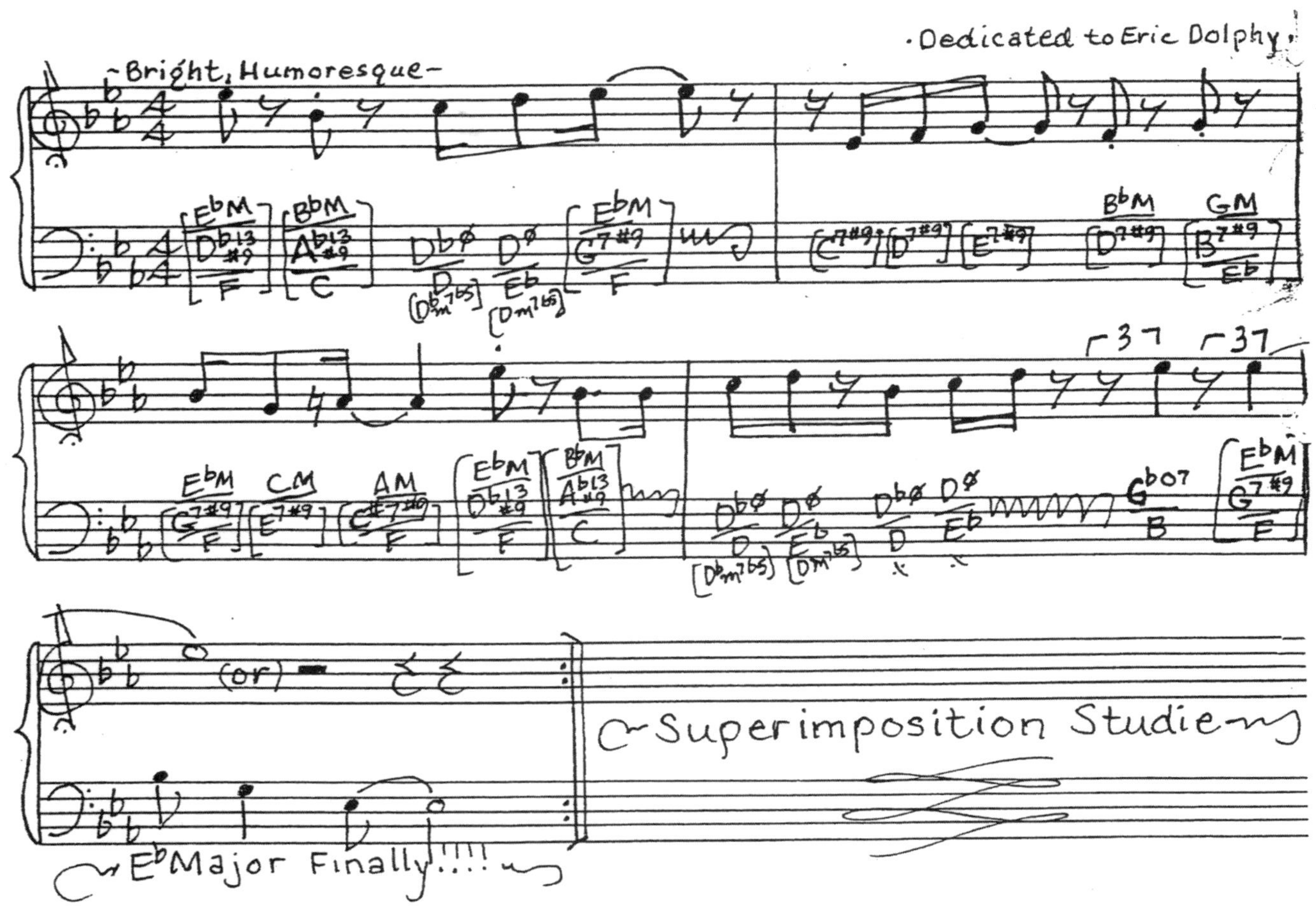

This Allegiance

This Allegiance (Continued)

7

S. Sx.

E.B.

Pno.

10

S. Sx.

E.B.

Pno.

This Time Last Spring

Tippy One Ahead

TOT

TOT (Continued)

8

Fl.

8

Pno.

13

Fl.

13

Pno.

18

Fl.

18

Pno.

TOT (Continued)

TOT (Continued)

Treasured Alliances

Treasures

Bb insts.
Latino
Dedicated to Chick Corea
.... and all humankind
4XS
etc

Triad

Triad

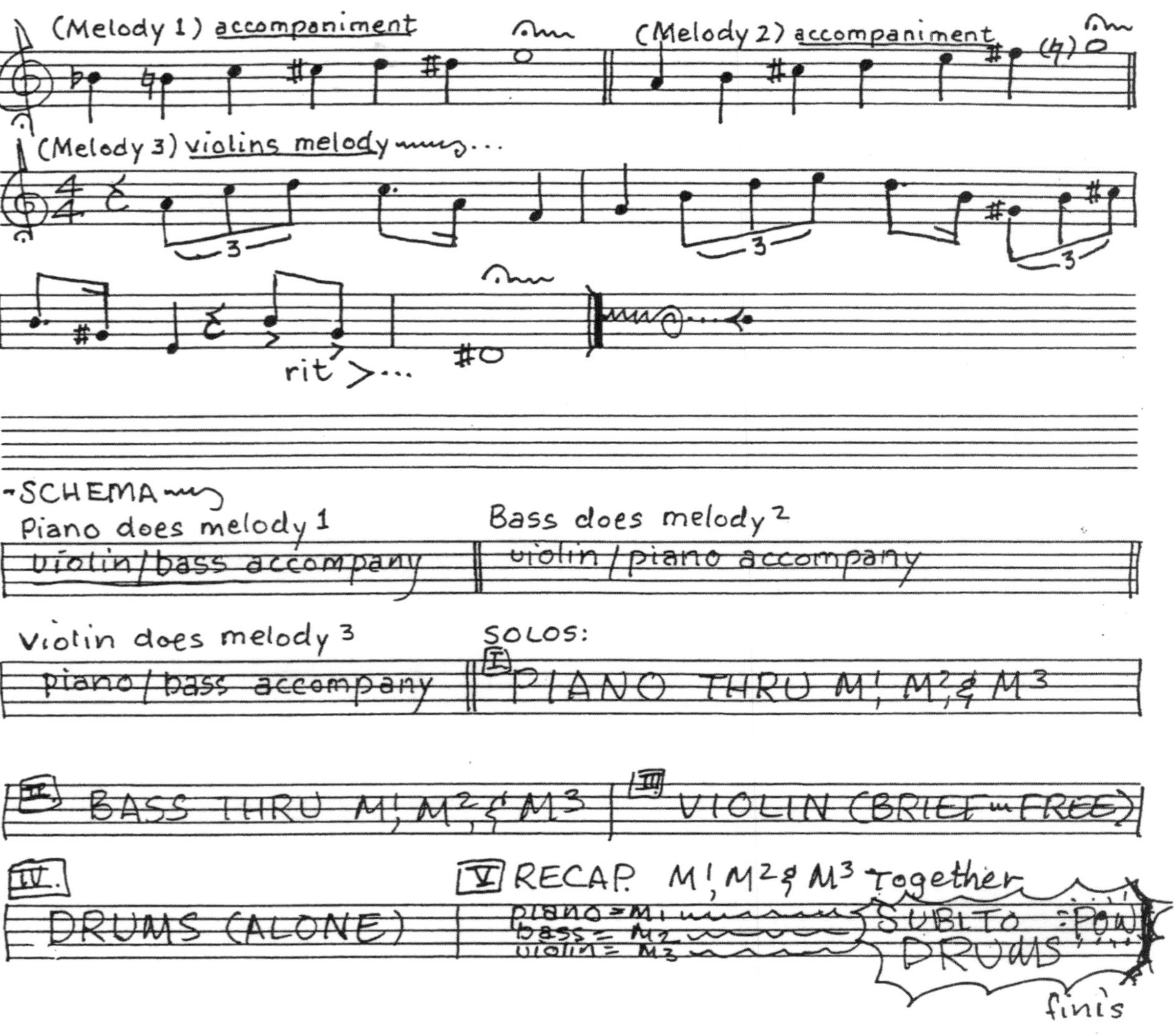
(Melody 1) accompaniment
(Melody 2) accompaniment
(Melody 3) violins melody...
rit ...
SCHEMA
Piano does melody 1
violin/bass accompany
Bass does melody 2
violin/piano accompany
violin does melody 3
piano/bass accompany
SOLOS:
I PIANO THRU M1, M2 & M3
II BASS THRU M1, M2 & M3
III VIOLIN (BRIEF FREE)
IV. DRUMS (ALONE)
V RECAP. M1, M2 & M3 Together
piano = M1
bass = M2
violin = M3
SUBITO POW DRUMS
finis

Tryptycht for Molly

Tryxsisia

Tryxsisia (Continued)

Tsimtsum

Oboe
Clarinet in Bb
Bass Clarinet
Cornet
Marimba
Piano
Violin 1
Violin 2
Violin 3
Violoncello

Tsimtsum (Continued)

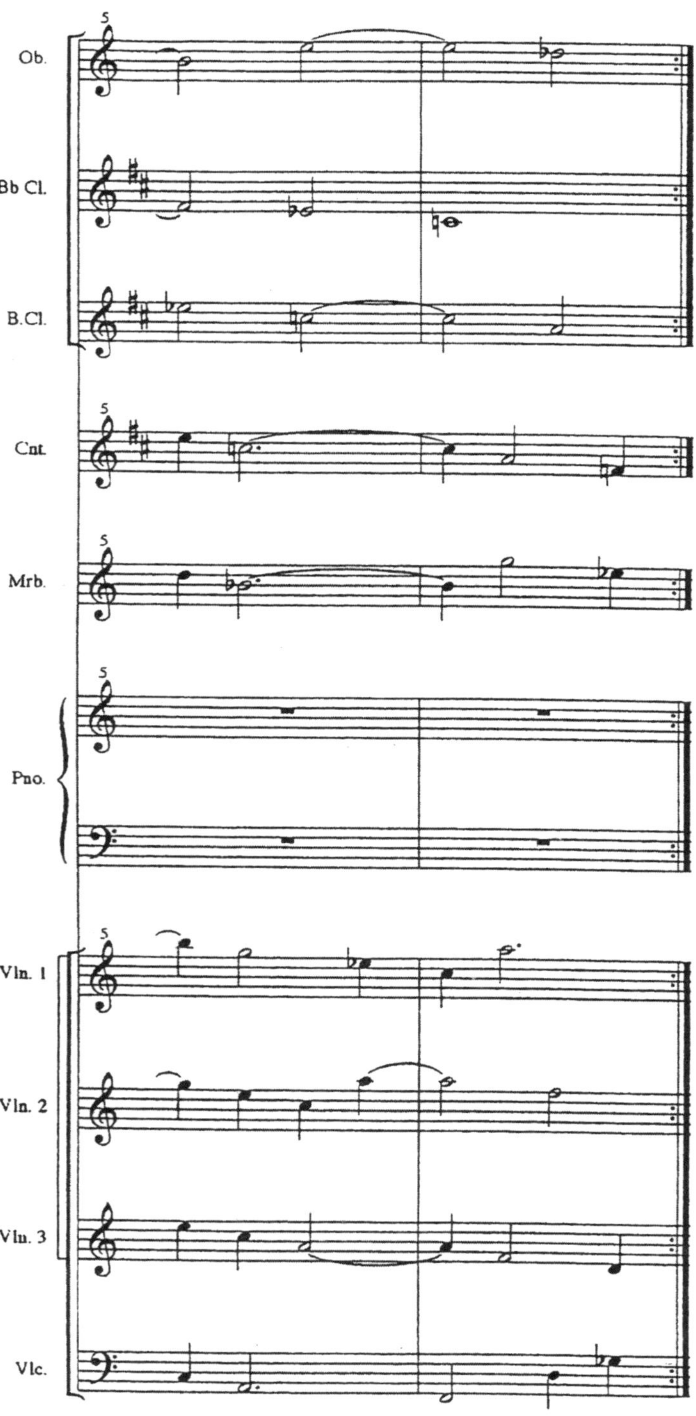

Turn Left, You Can't Miss It

Turning Point Anthem

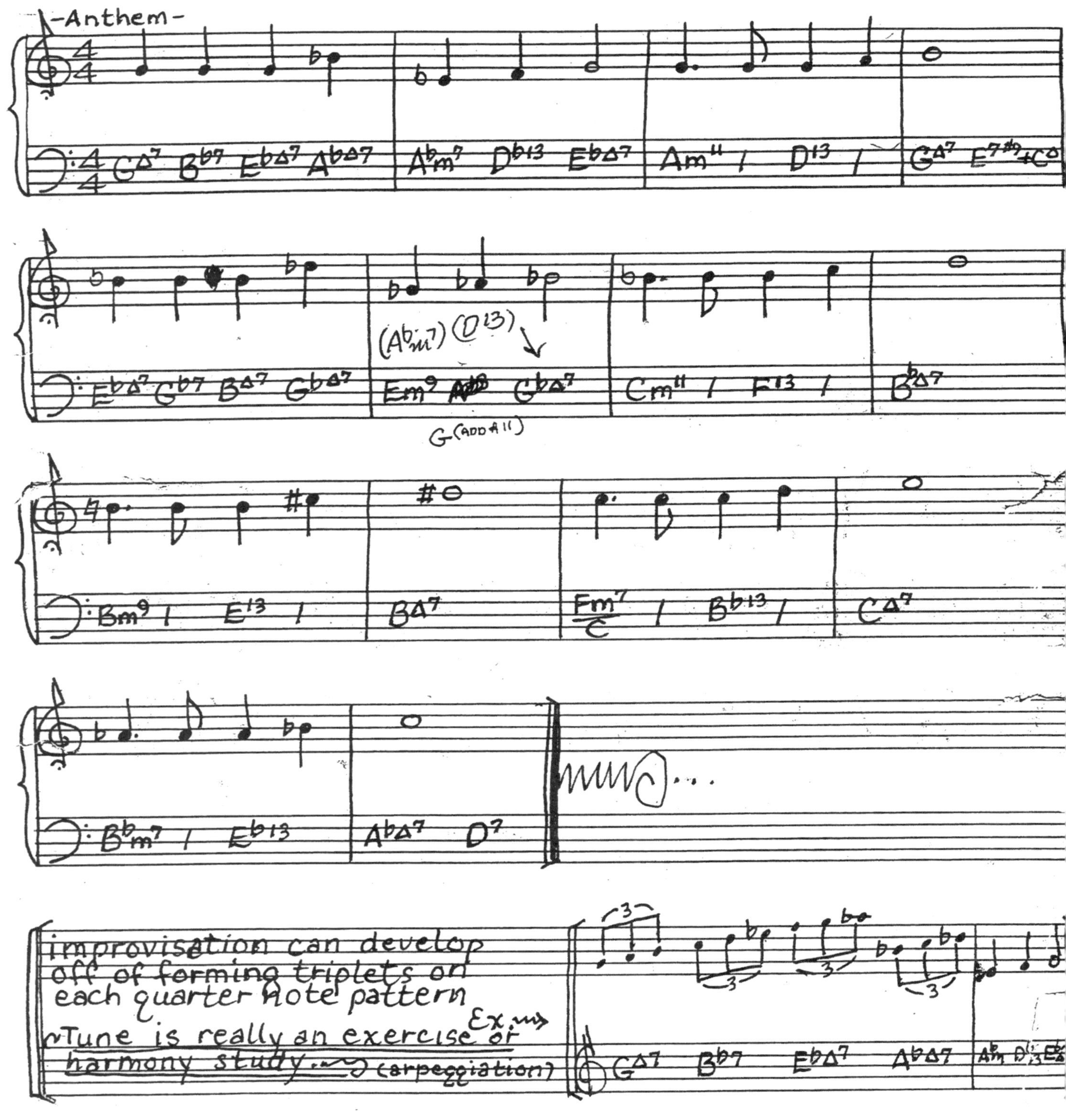

When Where Is Lost

Wraith Dance

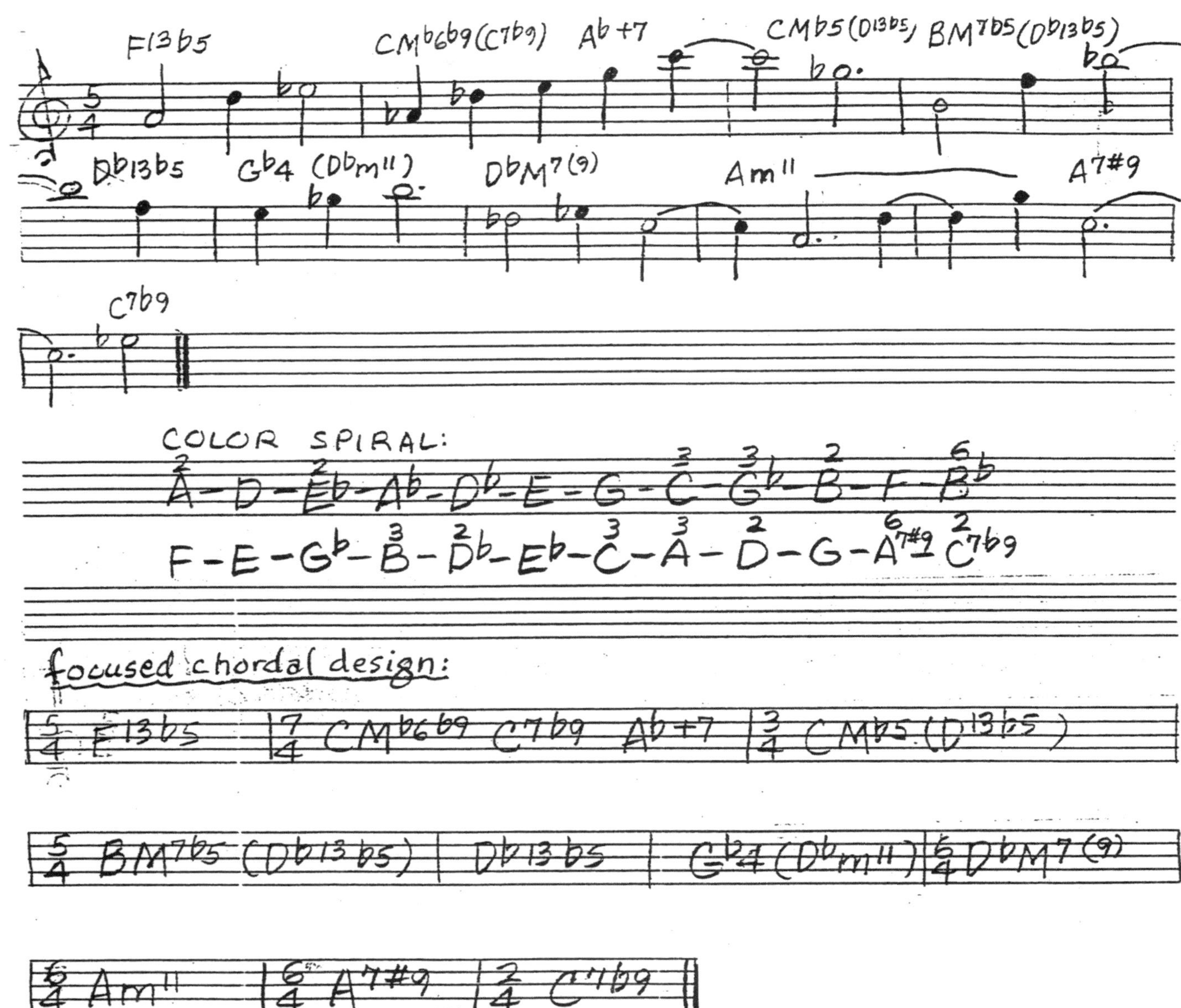

You Bet Your Life/That's Shu Biz

Bb inst

You I Love

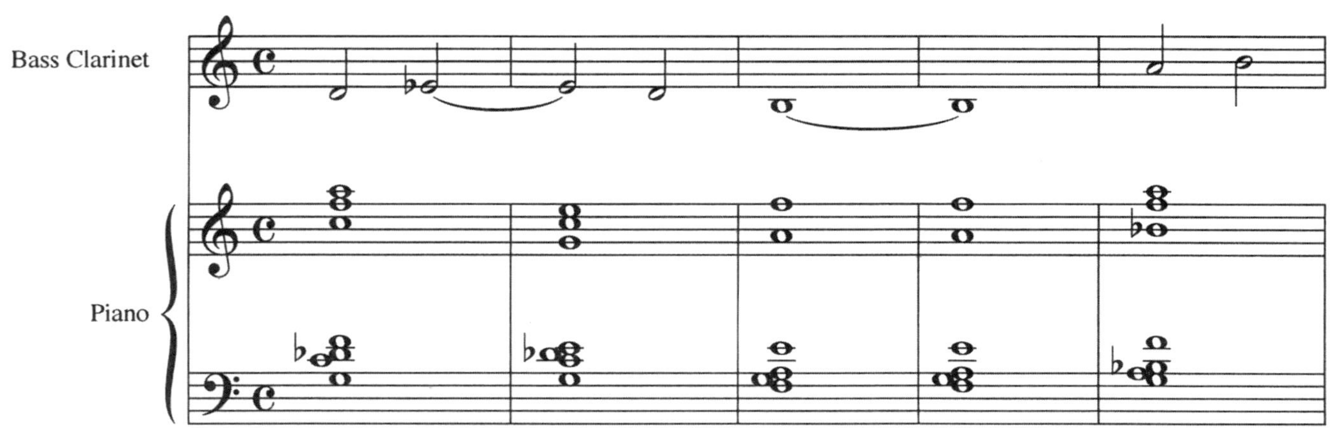

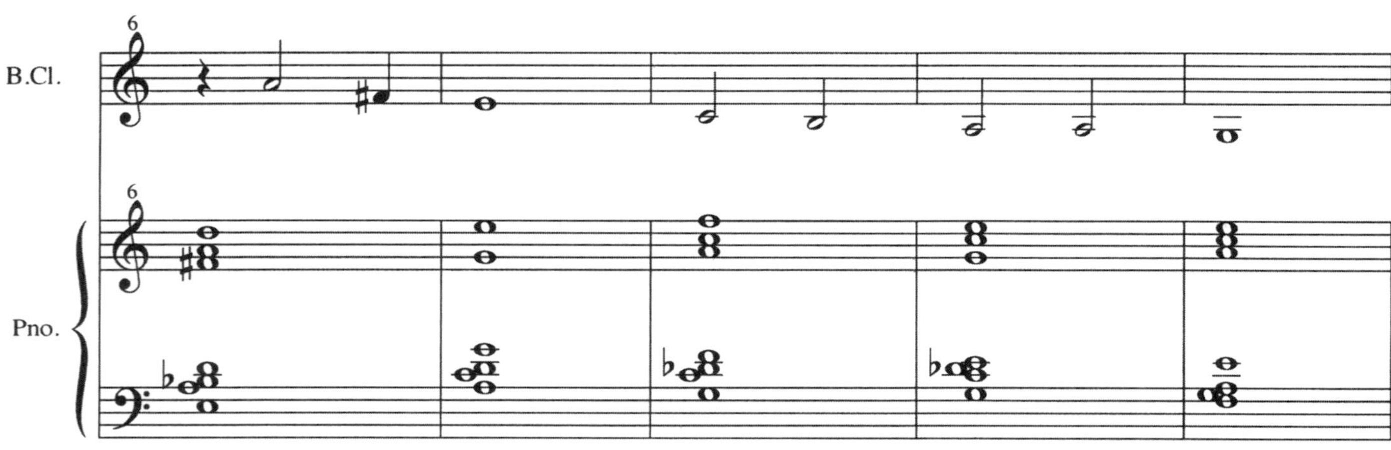

You I Love (Continued)

GRAPHIC COMPOSITIONS

You will see examples of my graphic compositions in the pages that follow. I would like to see some of these sculpted/molded in polymer-like, organic materials and placed on a stage where dancers, musicians and possibly audience members create a piece in and around the environment the graphics present.

The titles of the Graphic Compositions or Hard Copies in the order they appear in this section:

Ends Open for the Female in Me (Dedicated to M.C. Escher)
Nimbus
Roy McBride in Four Places
She/Woman
Snellie
Sound Town I
Sound Town II
The Day – Mimi

Some thoughts on how these might be used are the following:

I see "Snellie" as a Calderesque-like mobile to be sculpted/molded in polymer-like organic media and hung in a selected environment. Then, dancers, performance artists of varying design would walk through/amidst the sculpture singing, doing textual things, dancing, possibly along with audience members and/or this mobile could be accompanied with an instrumental ensemble—say of oboe, cello, bassoon, and voice, or some other combination. The "Snellie" hard copy is about 1/75th of the actual size when constructed. Of course, I'm not a three dimensional artist and it would be a thrilling challenge to collaborate with a sculptor (student) to bring "Snellie" to reality as a three-dimensional music composition.

Note: There are four separate hanging pieces.
The large snail-like morph.
The open donut morph with the music efflorescing.
The largest donut morph that would hang above the snail-like morph.
The donut morph at the bottom right.

"She/Woman" could be on clear gel or colored gels (of varying colors) and projected on a surface of varying textural media and music can accompany switches and changes of "her" movements . . . she could go spinning and spinning and spinning, etc.

"Sound Town I" and "Sound Town II" are two samples of topographical/architectural soundscaping. These pieces could be realized through the use of gels. Also, possibly being projected on hanging cloth which drapes and folds giving this already kinetic form more metamobility. These, too, can be accompanied with music, dancers (draped in cloth), geometric shapes, etc.

"A Portrait of Roy McBride in Four Places" is a musical portrait of a friend and colleague, local poet Roy McBride. It can be turned in four positions, each one can be *juxtaported to four different places. Each place can be played musically or represented separately by varying disciplines: dance, poetry/spoken word or integrated with some or all of the aforementioned disciplines. These, too, can be developed in modular mobile constructions and could be pushed/blown to move in pendulum fashion. Or, could be done on gel and moved to each juxtaported position and played accordingly like the chance works of John Cage or Lucier. In other words, one could order a series of positions the way Schoenberg ordered a tone row in serial progression and then realize different permutations.

Note: Juxtaportation: To carry, send, or be sent from one place to another for comparison and/or contrast. (Carei Thomas' definition)

"Ends Open for the Female in Me" (Dedicated to M.C. Escher) is an outgrowth of the earlier "Sound Towns" and has in some way come through the Roy McBride work to evolve into a referentially Escher kind of piece. It can be developed three dimensionally borrowing from the "Snellie" ideas (polymer plastics), I think. Or, this could be copied on gel like the "Sound Town" pieces idea and projected. THIS ONE HAS MANY POSSIBILITIES THAT CAN ONLY BE REALIZED THROUGH COLLABORATIVE EXCHANGE AND INCLUSION fostered by this embryonic notion. I would be interested in an activity involving artists with acumen in different media. THIS ONE CRIES OUT FOR THOSE WHO WORK IN CERTAIN MEDIA TO BRING IT TO FRUITION.

Note: Computer systems have become more persuasive allowing now for more agility in bringing about some of the technical manipulations beckoned to in the above descriptions. It would be fun to get with knowledgeable computer people to have them use techniques other than mere "clear gel" use.

Ends Open for the Female in Me
(Dedicated to M.C. Escher)

Nimbus

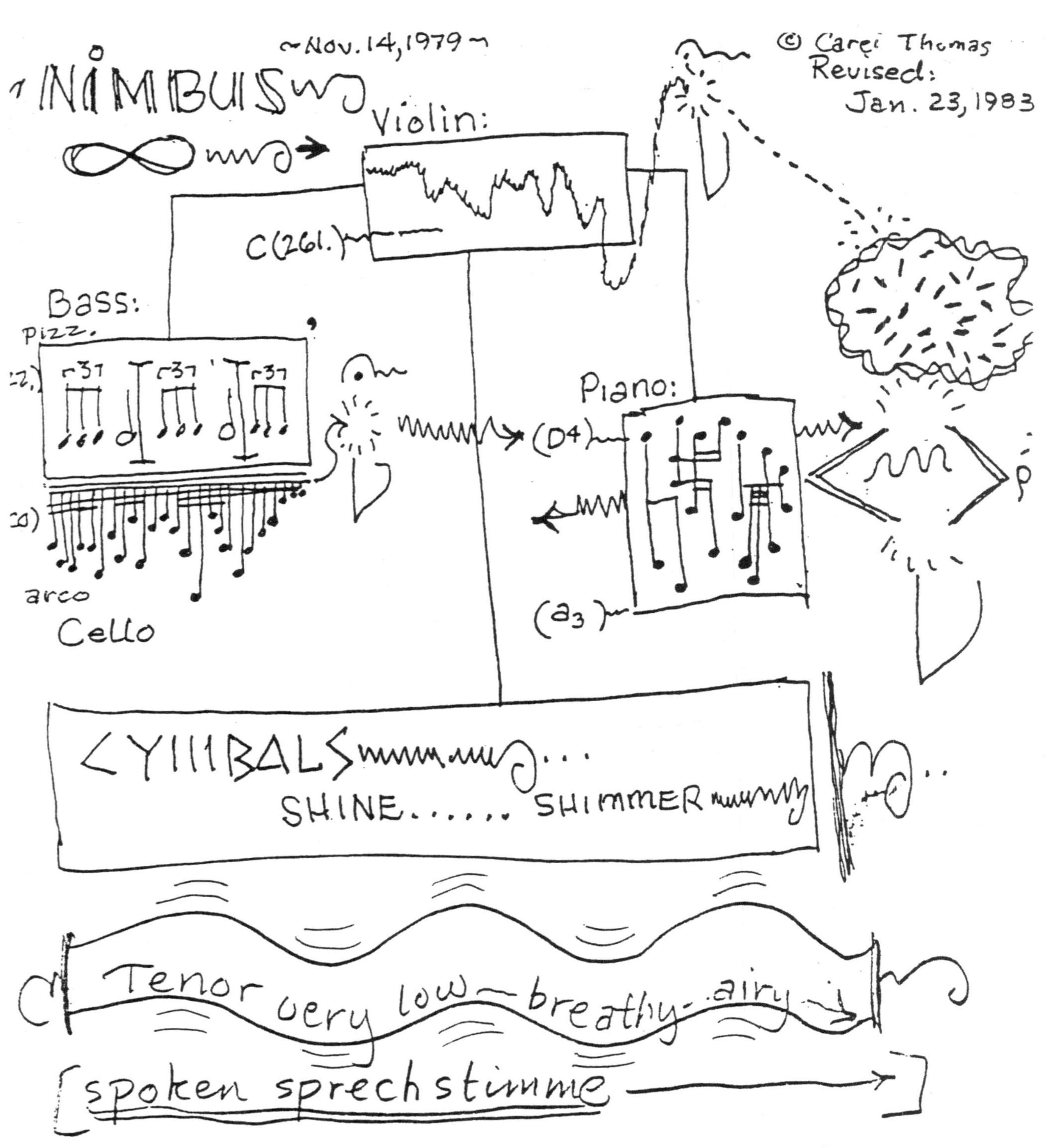

~Nov. 14, 1979~
NIMBUS
© Carei Thomas
Revised:
Jan. 23, 1983
Violin:
C(261.)
Bass:
pizz.
Piano:
(D4)
(a3)
arco
Cello
CYMBALS
SHINE...... SHIMMER
Tenor very low—breathy—airy
spoken sprechstimme

Roy McBride in Four Places

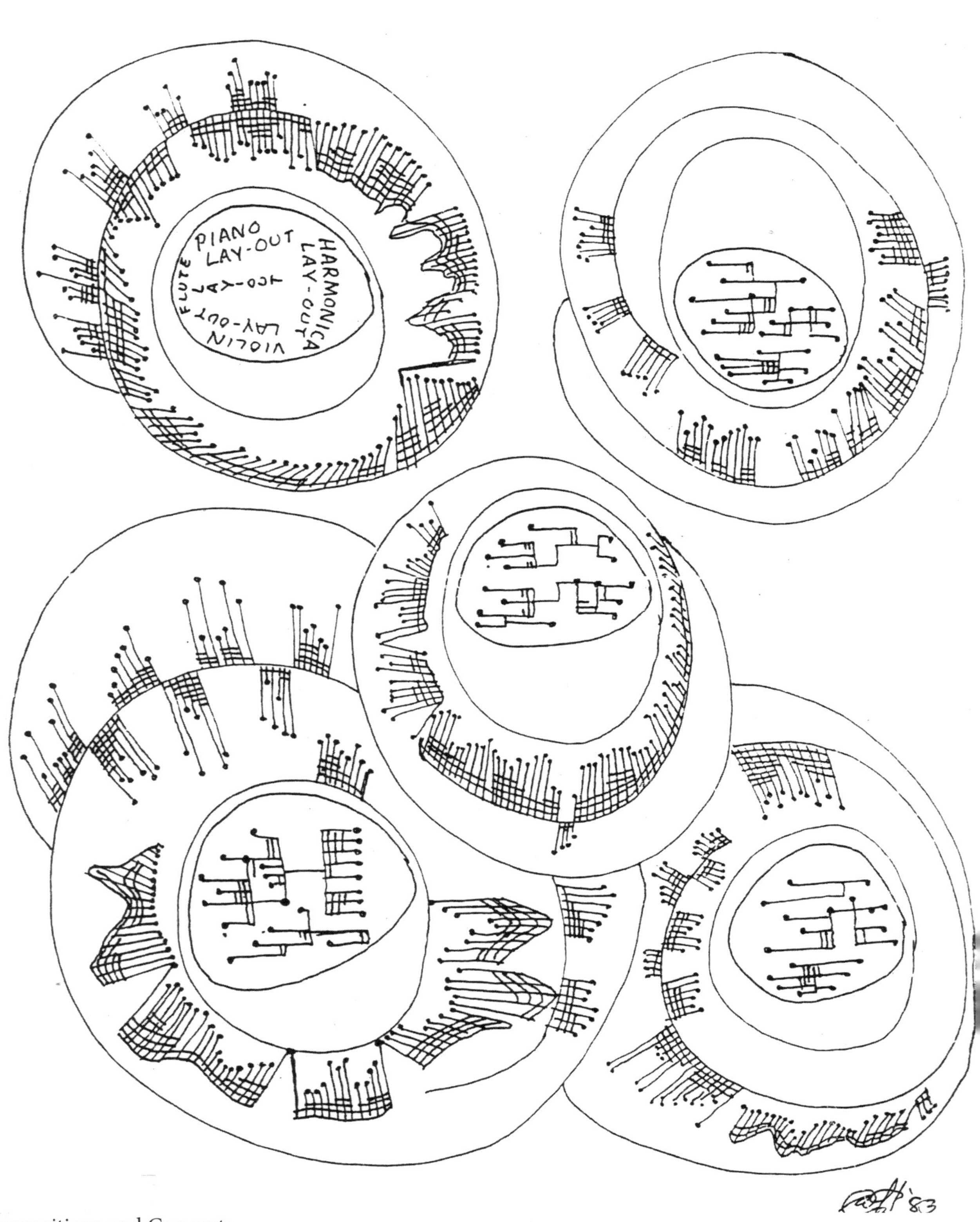

She/Woman

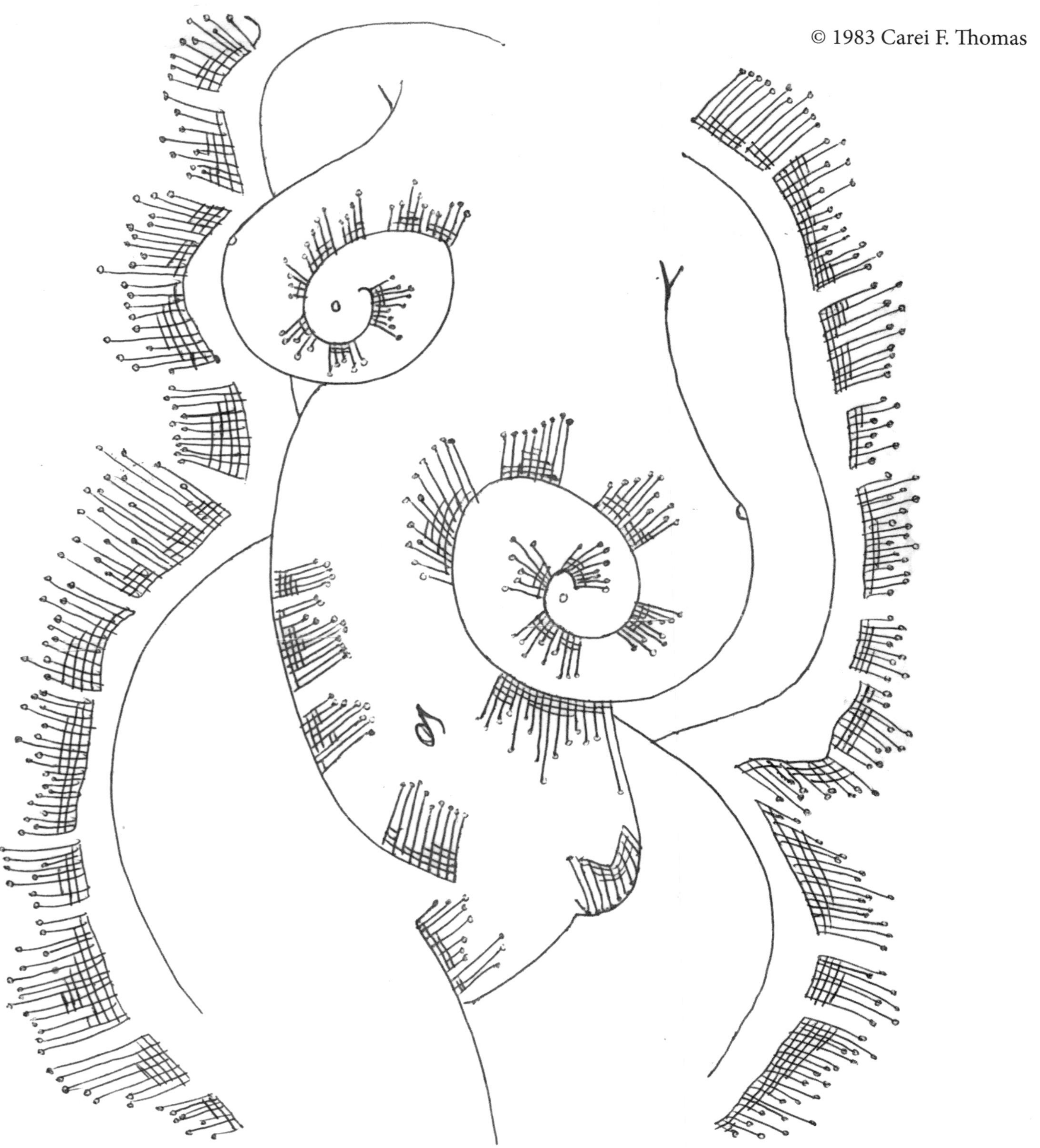

Snellie

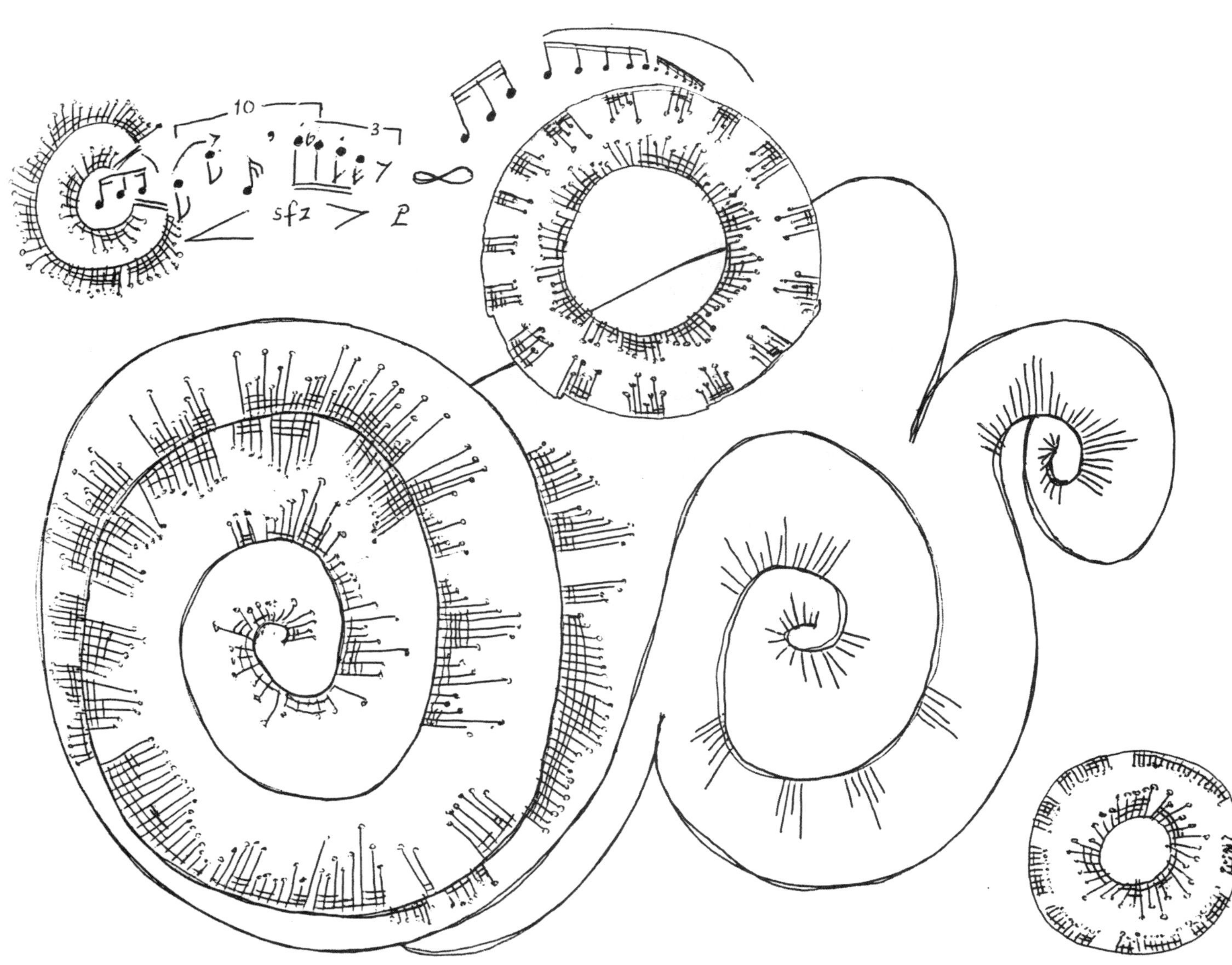

Sound Town I

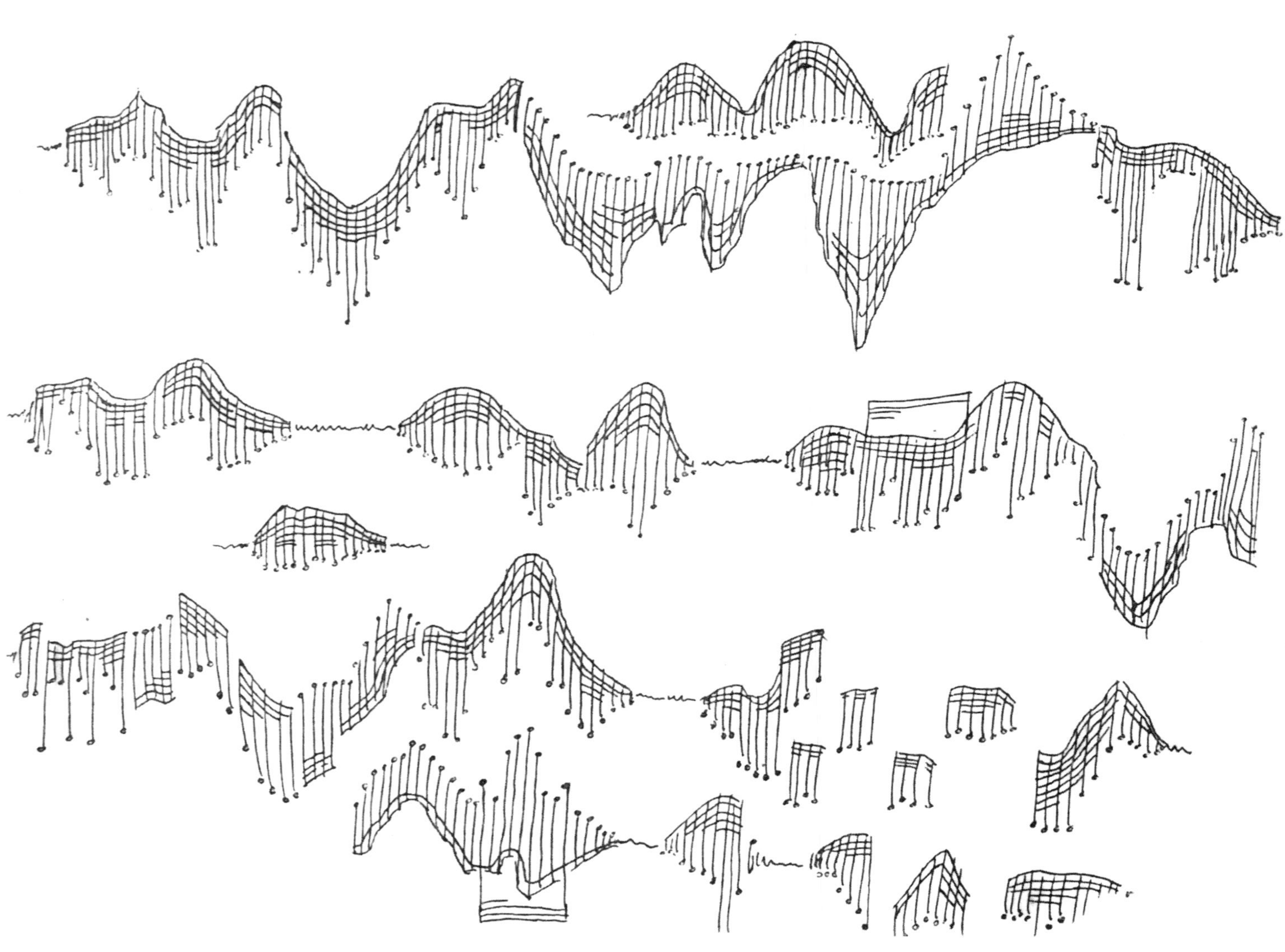

Sound Town II

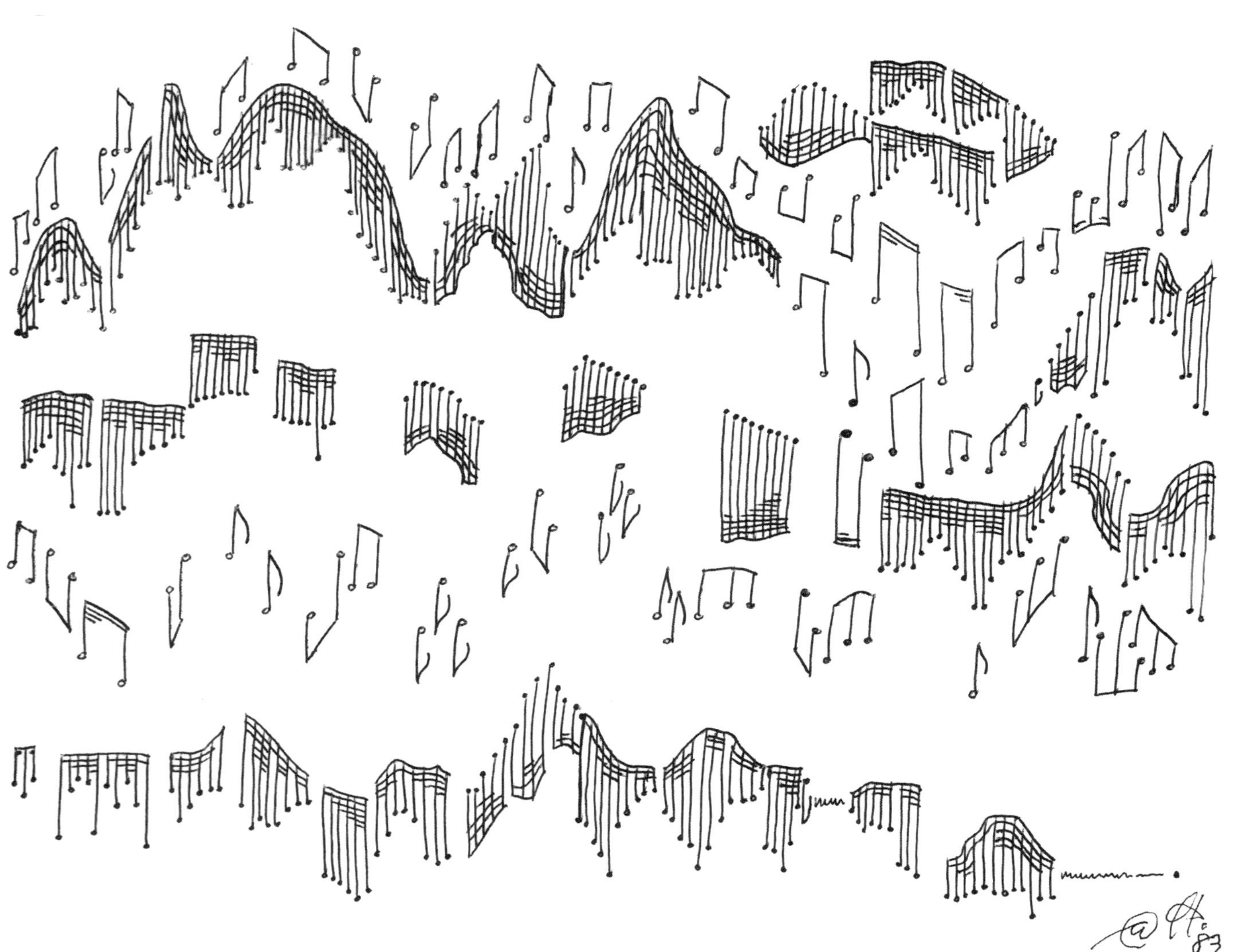

The Day—Mimi

© Carei F. Thomas

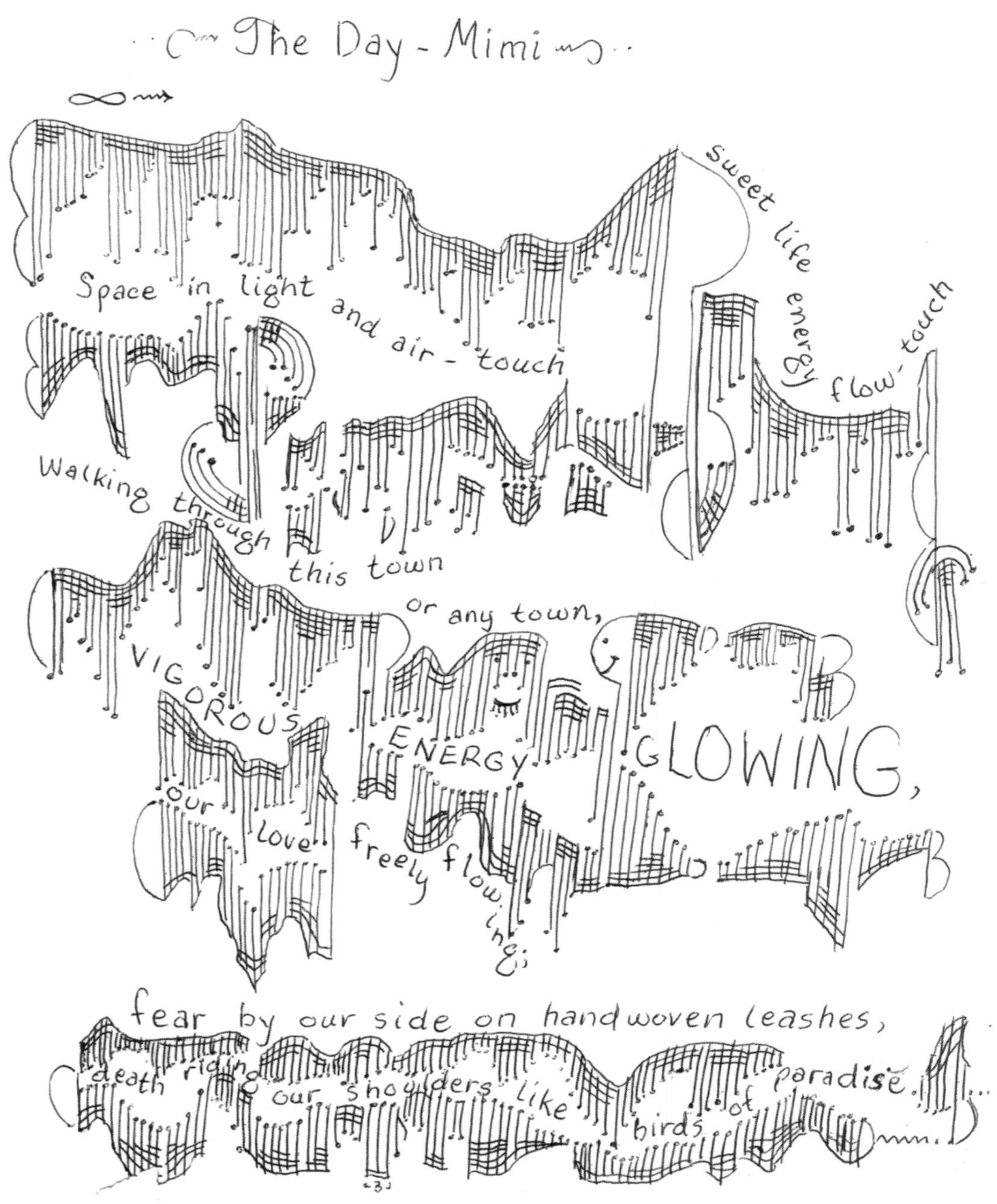

Permission given by Roy McBride to use his poem embedded in this graphic composition.

SYNTH-CHORAL WORKS

My synth-choral works were created with the Finale software program. I am not a vocalist so some of these ranges and connecting patterns may not be feasible for actual chorus singers. I encourage vocalists to adapt these songs for their voice ranges. I started these choral writings around the same time I took an interest in the "smoke and mirrors" of acoustical/electronic considerations. They were originally intended to be used as tonal fabrics or soundscapes.

Some of my Synth-Choral works were presented publicly when Ta'Coumba Aiken (a Twin Cities visual artist) and myself collaborated on a Minnesota Exhibition Artist Program (MAEP) at the Minneapolis Institute of Art in the Fall of 2007 and Spring of 2008. When I looked at Ta'Coumba's artwork for this exhibit, I was drawn synesthetically to seeing the sound of the voices of my culture. The subject matter of Ta'Coumba's reliefs were so vivid that, to me, they resonated with all living things. I could hear my synth-choral works conjoining with Ta'Coumba's multi-dimensional works. Then I worked with Steve Goldstein, a master of percussion and sound design, to give a robust and churning life-force to the interiority of the vocal compositions, connecting them viscerally to the visual works.

Baahmidjian Scaal

Baahmidjian Scaal (Continued)

Baahmidjian Scaal (Continued)

Familiar Fields

Familiar Fields (Continued)

Familiar Fields (Continued)

Fresh Air of Majesta

© Carei F. Thomas

Soprano 1

Soprano 2

Soprano 3

Alto 1

Alto 2

Tenor 1

Tenor 2

Baritone

Bass

Fresh Air of Majesta (Continued)

6

S 1

S 2

S 3

A 1

A 2

T 1

T 2

B

B

Fresh Air of Majesta (Continued)

11

S 1

S 2

S 3

A 1

A 2

T 1

T 2

B

B

Fresh Air of Majesta (Continued)

Hidden Peaces

Helix for Spiral Building I

Helix for Spiral Building I (Continued)

Helix for Spiral Building I (Continued)

Helix for Spiral Building I (Continued)

Kind Peace

© Carei F. Thomas

Kind Peace (Continued)

Ordinaire

Ordinaire (Continued)

Ordinaire (Continued)

5

Ob.

Pno.

CAlt.

S

A

T

B

B

Ordinaire (Continued)

Ordinaire (Continued)

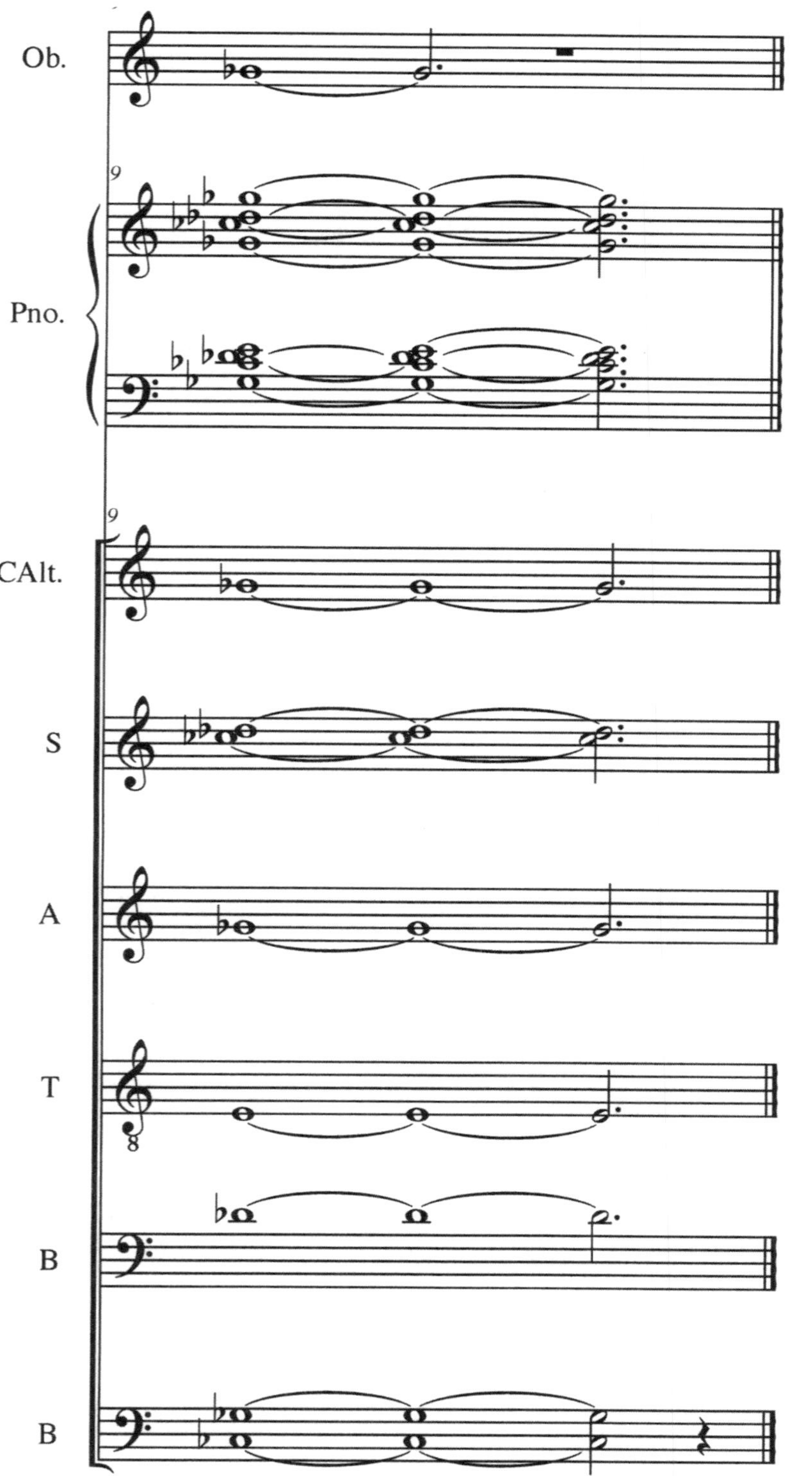

Slymn Hymn

Slymn Hymn (Continued)

Slymn Hymn (Continued)

Slymn Hymn (Continued)

Slymn Hymn (Continued)

RUMINATIONS

Some of what follows are cells or fragments of written material along with beginnings and/or studies that resulted in songs you will find in the main part of the book. Here are a few notes:

Alwhere—use of a static antiphony. This is a way to extend a piece using a controlled improvisational grid which allows for expansion of a single tone and/or a "scrambled" improvisation.

Cartoon Fragma is just that—refer to the Concepts Explanations and note the explanation of scrambles, color rows and static antiphonies.

Choose Choice is an example of what later became a song, in this case it became "Roagjyii-Ahl."

Color Rows—refer to Concept Explanations.

DeFacto—an early experiment of using an alphabet matrix. I came upon this approach to using literal etymological data as a ground from which to draw melodic and harmonic definition. See Concepts Explanations.

Dream for Times Out of Mind—another experimental composition using staggered metrics/paradigm matrices. See Concepts Explanations.

Eric Only Knew—similar to "Choose Choice" except it has a palindromic overall definition.

From Five On Down To Four—one of my first experiments with staggered metrical definition.

Glide I—used to support harmonically the song "Awestruck Waters of Antiquity."

Juxtaportation—see insert on song page.

Live Wire—an early trope.

MagicMysticMaestroMentor—these are the extensions of the song you will find in the main part of the book.

Morse Code—a sample of poemmetry.

Period—an amalgam of conceptual material.

Stellium—a "Do what you want widdit" study.

The Reconstruction of Light—includes photochromokinesis, a couple solo brief realities, second movement of the song Juxtaportation, and a phononomaly.

When I Look Back—My original neighborhood like some (un)winding road has brought me HERE making each Brief Reality a treasure, a divine protection which teaches me to nurture the brilliance and candor of each "life's moment," another precious thing born without wings—ALWHERE.

Alwhere: Anthem
(Performance Design Reduction)

Alwhere: Static Antiphony

STATIC ANTIPHONY (1st Entry)

cellos	4	C	3	G#	2	B	1	E	2	G	3	A#	4	D# :
viola / flute I	C	3	G#	2	B	1	E	2	G	3	A#	4	D#	4
flute II / violin I	3	G#	2	B	1	E	2	G	3	A#	4	D#	4	C :
violin II + III	G#	2	B	1	E	2	G	3	A#	4	D#	4	C	3 :
Bb clarinet	Bb	2	C#	1	F#	2	A	3	C	4	F	4	D	3 :
Eb alto sax	2	Ab	1	Db	2	E	3	G	4	C	4	A	3	F :
tenor sax I + II	2	C#	1	F#	2	A	3	C	4	F	4	D	3	G :
Eb baritone sax	Ab	1	Db	2	E	3	G	4	C	4	A	3	F	2 :
French Horn	1	B	2	D	3	F	4	Bb	4	G	3	Eb	2	Gb :

Cartoon Fragma

PICKLES (CARTOON XII)

3	2		4					
F	G	[≈3≈]	D	G^b	[≈4≈]	A	A	A
3	2		4					
G	A	[≈4≈]	E	A^b	[≈3≈]	C	C	C
3	2		4	3				
D	E	[≈2≈]	B	E^b	[≈3≈]	G^b	G	$G^\#$

UNTITLED CARTOON

2	2		3	3						2	2
B^b	B^b	[≈3≈]	B^b	B^b	[≈4≈]	B^b	B	C	[≈2≈]	$C^\#$	$C^\#$
2	2		3	3						2	2
C	C	[≈3≈]	C	C	[≈4≈]	C	$C^\#$	D	[≈2≈]	$D^\#$	$D^\#$

UNTITLED II

2	2		3	3		2	2	2		2	2
B^b	B^b	[≈4≈]	B^b	B^b	[≈3≈]	B^b	B	C	[≈2≈]	$C^\#$	$C^\#$
2	2		3	3						2	2
C	C	[≈4≈]	C	C	[≈3≈]	C	$C^\#$	D	[≈2≈]	$D^\#$	$D^\#$

Cartoon Fragma

Cartoon XVII: Somethin' Monk'y (After Filonov, Before Kandinsky)

Carei F. Thomas
2001

Note: The standard notation that follows this page is an approximate representation of the matrix shown below.

The configuration - "≈ ≈" - I call "scrambles" and indicates for the instrumentalists to freely improvise with no thought to tonality but rather to emphasize timbral expression. Then, I add metric considerations. A number within a scramble designates its duration (i.e., ≈ ≈ with a 3 in it [≈ 3 ≈] equals three beats of free improvisation).

Instrumentalists: Feel free to mix and match any or all of the "cartoon rows" as humor and mischief so moves you.

3	2		4					
F	G	[≈3≈]	D	Gb	[≈4≈]	A	A	A
3	2		4					
G	A	[≈3≈]	E	Ab	[≈4≈]	B	B	B
3	2		4					
D	E	[≈3≈]	B	Eb	[≈4≈]	Gb	Gb	Gb
3	2			2				
C	D	[≈4≈]	A	C#	[≈5≈]	E	E	E

Cartoon Fragma

SIDE SHOW (25 beats)

D# – E – F – [m2m] – G – [m3m] – D – G♭ [m4m] – A – A – A

(B♭) F – F# – G – [m2m] – A – [m3m] – E – A♭ [m4m] – B – B – B

(E♭) C – C# – D – [m2m] – E – [m3m] – B – E♭ [m4m] – G♭ – G♭ – G♭

QUESYI'S DREAM (25 beats)

B♭ – B♭ [m3m] – B♭ – B♭ – [m4m] – B♭ – B – C – [m2m] – C# – C#

(B♭) C – C – [m3m] – C – C – [m4m] – C – C# – D – [m2m] – D# – D#

(E♭) G – G – [m3m] – G – G – [m4m] – G – G# – A – [m2m] – A# – A#

Harmelodic SWEET CRUDE (17 beats)

[m2m] – X – E♭ – A – A – [m5m] – X – C – C – C# – F

X – E♭ – A – A – [m5m] – X – C – C – C# – [m2m]

E♭ – A – A – [m5m] – X – C – C – C# – F [m2m] – X

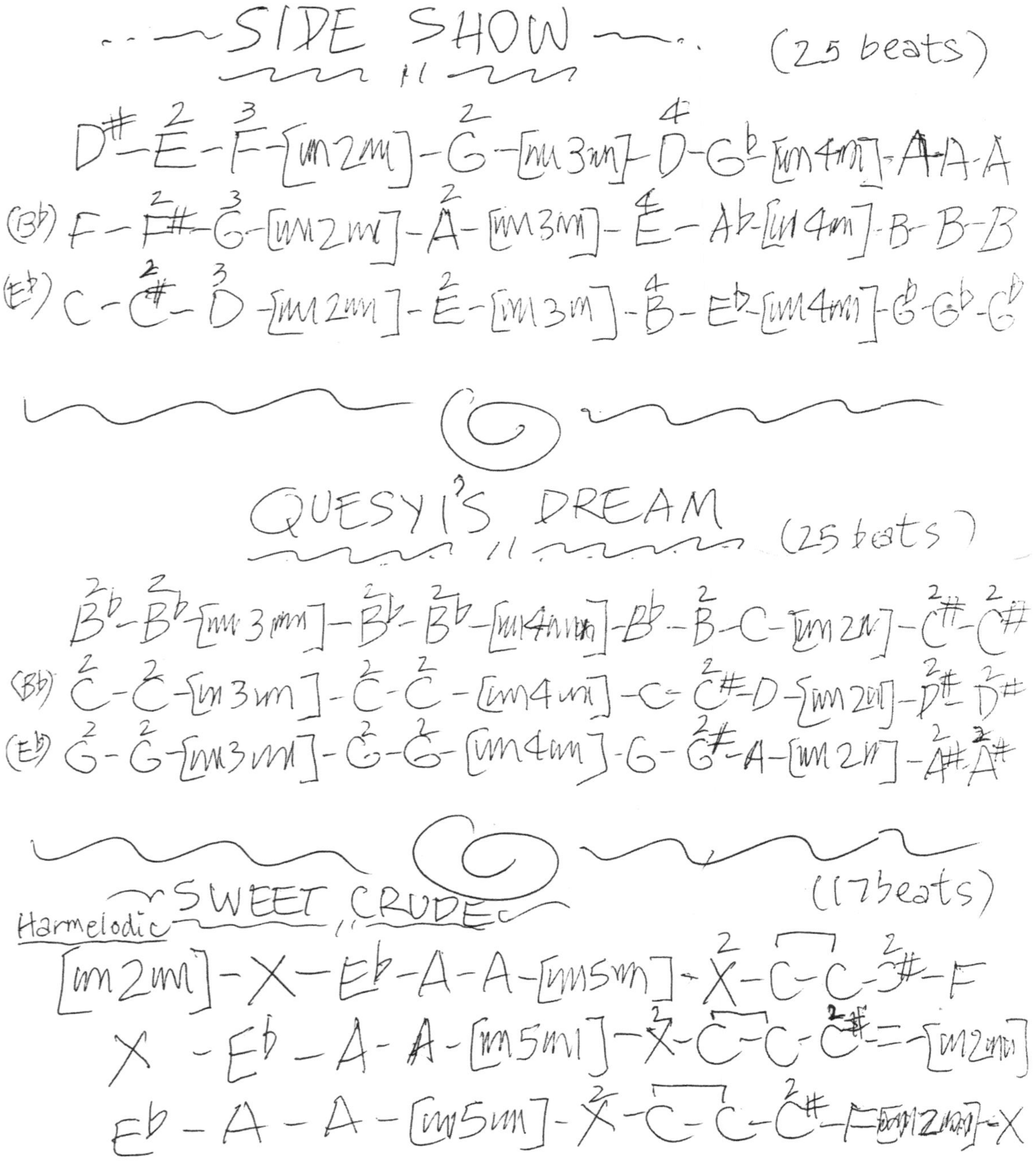

Choose Choice

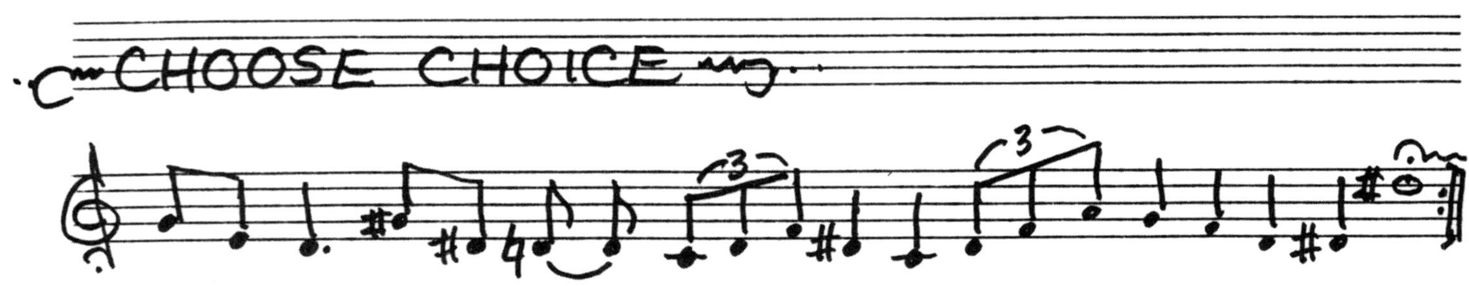

Color Rows for Spiral Building

Ia. SPIRAL ELEMENT CYCLE: (original)

violin (viola) ~..

C – F – Bb[2] – Eb – Ab[2] – Db – Gb[3] – B – E[3] – A – D[4] – G[2]

soprano sax ~.. (transposed)

D – G – C[2] – F – Bb[2] – Eb – Ab[3] – Db – Gb[3] – B – E[4] – A[2]

alto sax ~.. (transposed)

A – D – G[2] – C – F[2] – Bb – Eb[3] – Ab – Db[3] – Gb – B[4] – E[2]

tenor sax ~.. (transposed)

D – G – C[2] – F – Bb[2] – Eb – Ab[3] – Db – Gb[3] – B – E[4] – A[2]

bass violin ~..

C – F – Bb[2] – Eb – Ab[2] – Db – Gb[3] – B – E[3] – A – D[4] – G[2]

Ib. SPIRAL ELEMENT CYCLE: (staggered matrix) (emphasis on duration)

violin (viola) ~..

C – F – Bb[3] – Eb[2] – Ab – Db[3] – Gb – B – E – A[5] – D – G[2]

soprano sax ~..

D – G[3] – C[2] – F – Bb[2] – Eb – Ab – Db – Gb[5] – B – E[2] – A

alto sax ~..

A[3] – D[2] – G – C[2] – F – Bb – Eb – Ab[5] – Db – Gb[2] – B – E

tenor sax ~..

D[2] – G – C[2] – F – Bb – Eb – Ab[5] – Db – Gb[2] – B – E[3] – A

bass violin ~..

C – F[2] – Bb – Eb – Ab – Db[5] – Gb – B[2] – E – A[3] – D[2] – G

Color Rows for Spiral Building

Ic. SPIRAL ELEMENT CYCLE (staggered matrix) (emphasis on tonality

violin (viola)~..

C – F – Bb[3] – Eb[2] – Ab – Db[2] – Gb – B – E – A[5] – D[3] – G[2]

soprano sax~..

G – C – F[3] – Bb[2] – Eb – Ab[2] – Db – Gb – B – E[5] – A[3] – D[2]

alto sax~..

G – C – F[3] – Bb[2] – Eb – Ab[2] – Db – Gb – B – E[5] – A[3] – D[2]

tenor sax~..

F – Bb – Eb[3] – Ab[2] – Db – Gb[2] – B – E – A – D[5] – G[3] – C[2]

II. GLIDE:

Bb[4] – G – Eb – C – A[3] – F[3] – D[4] – Gb – B – E[2] – Db[2]

III. ENCHANTMENT:

C – A[4] – F – D[3] – Bb[5] – G – Eb – Db – Gb[2] – B[2] – E[6] (27 beats)

IV. PYRAMID:

♩=80 A – F[2] – G[3] – D[4] – Gb[5] – B[6] – Ab[5] – Db[4] – Bb[3] – C[2] – E

V. (For "We Are A River") → hook up w/ Gary's stuff economically~..

∞ D – B – G – E – C# – A – F# – Bb – Eb – Ab – F

tutti [4 |||| |||| |||| ||||] ~..

VI.

Eb[3] – Db – B – Gb[3] – Ab[2] – Bb – G – A – D[4] – C[2] – F[3]

Color Rows for Spiral Building

Colorscape Matrix

MATRIX I:

3			2		4			5		2	2
D	A	G#	D	G	A	F#	E	C	B	F	G#
		4		2	2	2			5	3	
B	F#	G#	E	A	D	D#	G	C	C#	A#	F
	2				5	3			4	3	
A	E	G	B	C#	G#	C	F#	E	F	A#	D
	3	5			2	2	2		4		
F	A#	C#	C	G	D#	D	A	E	G#	F#	B
	3	4			3	5				2	
D	A#	F	E	F#	C	G#	C#	B	G	E	A
2	2		5			4		2			3
G#	F	B	C	E	F#	A	G	D	C#	A#	D#

MATRIX II:

3			2		4			5		2	2
D#	A#	C#	D	G	A	F#	E	C	B	F	G#
		4		2	2	2			5	3	
B	F#	G#	E	A	D	D#	G	C	C#	A#	F
	2				5	3			4	3	
A	E	G	B	C#	G#	C	F#	E	F	A#	D
4	3		4			2		3			3
F	A#	C#	C	G	D#	D	A	E	G#	A#	B
		2		5			3	2	2	4	
D	A#	F	E	F#	C	G#	C#	B	G	E	A
	2	5		2		2	2		2		4
G#	F	B	C	E	F#	A	G	D	C#	A#	D#

Crowding Daylight

(B^{b}, fuschia, SUN, LEO)

Matrix:

Largo
Do several times and then: Go Sharp (or Flat) as row unwinds -- (intermittently-slowly - picking and choosing tones to "manipulate.")

Oboe	2 D	A	F	F	C	G	A$^{\#}$	2 G
	A	F	F	C	G	A$^{\#}$	2 G	2 D
French Horn	F	F	C	G	A$^{\#}$	2 G	2 D	A
Violin	F	C	G	A$^{\#}$	2 G	2 D	A	F
Violin	C	G	A$^{\#}$	2 G	2 D	A	F	F
Viola	G	A$^{\#}$	2 G	2 D	A	F	F	C
Cello	A$^{\#}$	2 G	2 D	A	F	F	C	G
Bass	2 G	2 D	A	F	F	C	G	A$^{\#}$

"OUT OF TIME"

Matrix:
Bass Ostinato:

B	A	G	B	F	G	C	F$^{\#}$	E	(G)
2	|____	____|	2		-	|____	____|	3	

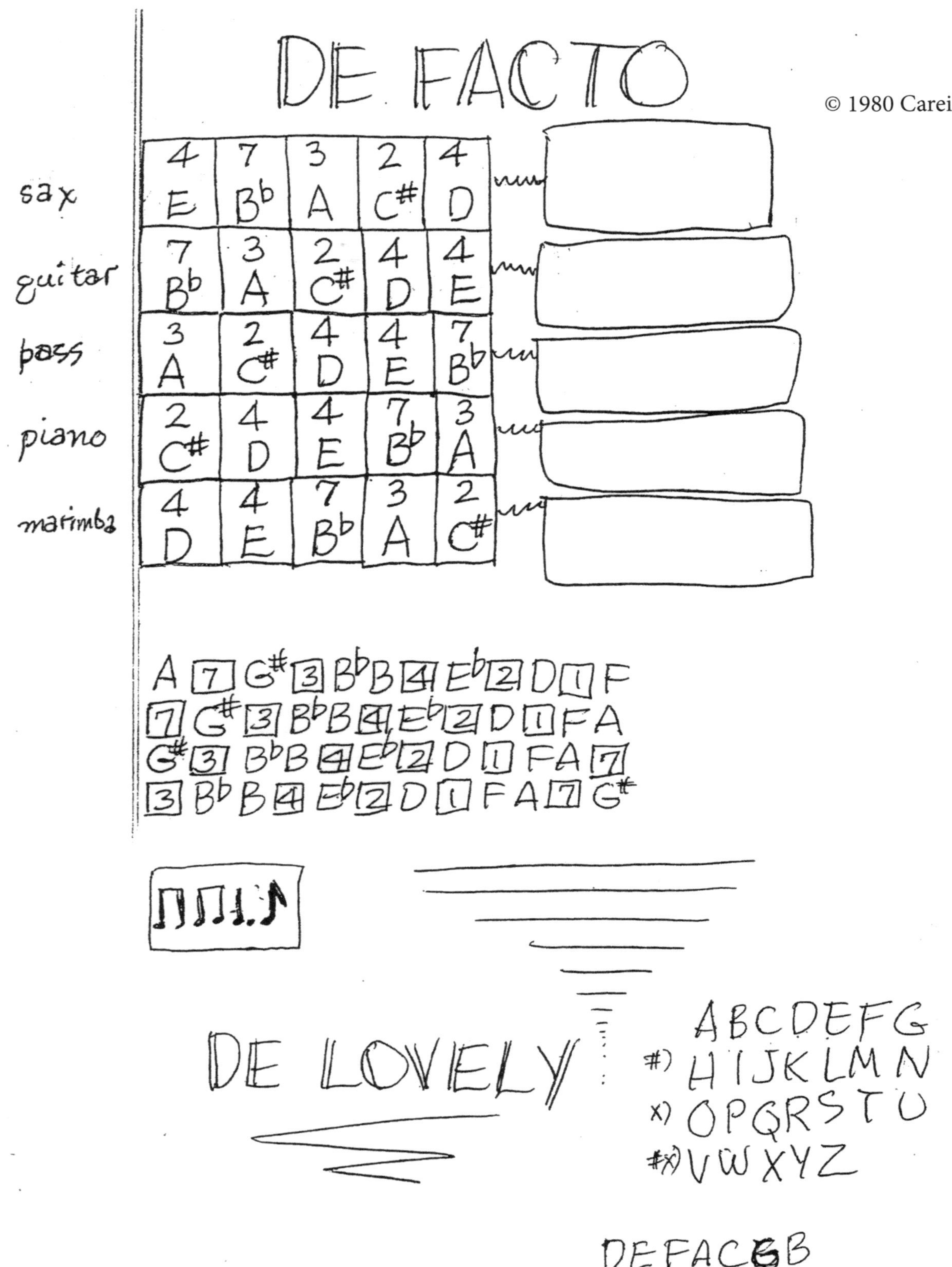
DE FACTO
sax
guitar
bass
piano
marimba
4 7 3 2 4
E B♭ A C# D
7 3 2 4 4
B♭ A C# D E
3 2 4 4 7
A C# D E B♭
2 4 4 7 3
C# D E B♭ A
4 4 7 3 2
D E B♭ A C#
DE LOVELY
ABCDEFG
#) HIJKLMN
x) OPQRSTU
#x) VWXYZ
DEFACGB
4561375

DREAM FOR TIMES OUT OF MIND
C. F. THOMAS
SEPT. 5, 1988
piano
introduction
piano
tutti
A
B
C oboe improvisation section: marimba/piano
BASSOON/TUBA 7:6:6:7 (13) figures
POINTILLICISM
JAGGED ATONALITY
D bassoon/trombone duet: oboe exit ~ enter guitar
PERCUSSION AND PIANO-HARP ACCOMPANIMENT
SPARSE... SWEEPING
E piano solo: percussion/marimba exit (lay out)
OBOE AND TUBA ACCOMPANIMENT

Dream for Times Out of Mind

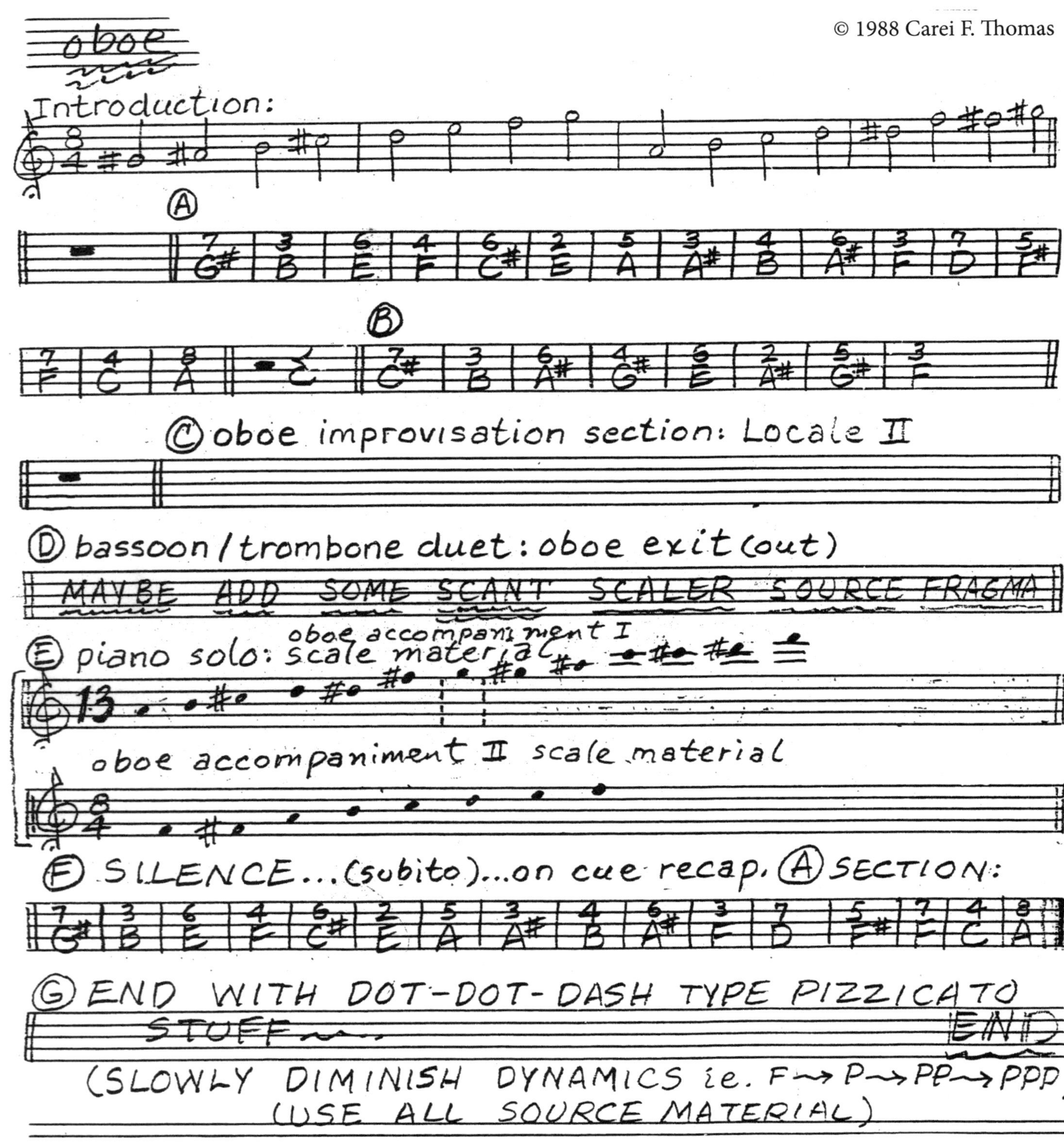

Dream for Times Out of Mind (Continued)

bassoon

Introduction:

(A)

7 D | 3 D | 6 G# | 4 B | 6 G | 2 G | 5 C# | 3 F# | 4 G | 6 D | 3 G# | 7 G# | 5 C | 7 A

4 D# | 8 D# ||

(B)

3 B | 6 A# | 4 G# | 6 E | 2 A# | 5 G# | 3 F | 7 C# ||

(C) oboe improvisation section: bassoon/tuba accompaniment

I.:

13 (6) (7)

(7) (6)

II.:

THEN LET FIGURE OBLITURATE INTO A KIND OF ACCOMPANIED IMPROVISATION... LISTEN/GIVE

(D) bassoon/trombone duet:

CAN USE SOURCE MATERIAL FROM OBOE SOLO ...AND/OR SCALE STUFF~..

(E) piano solo: bassoon exit (lay out)

OBOE AND TUBA WILL ACCOMPANY~..

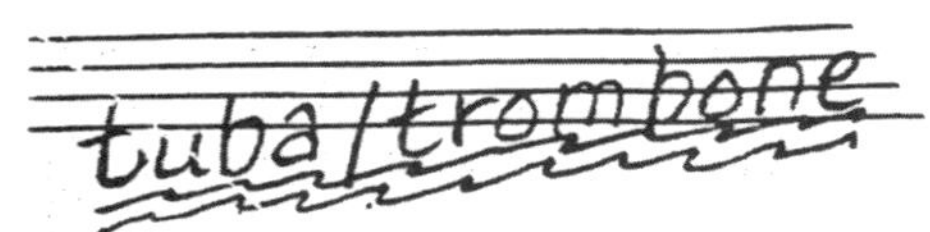

Introduction:

8/4

Ⓐ

7 A | 3 C# | 6 D | 4 F# | 6 D | 2 F# | 5 G | 3 B | 4 C | 6 G# | 3 G | 7 D# | 5 G | 7 D# | 4 D | 8 A#

Ⓑ

6 A# | 4 G# | 6 E | 2 A# | 5 G# | 3 F | 7 C# | 3 B

Ⓒ oboe improvisation section: bassoon/tuba accompaniment

I.:

13 (6) … (7) …

(7) … (6) … 3X

II.:

5/4 … REPEAT SEVERAL TIMES

THEN LET FIGURE OBLITURATE INTO A KIND OF ACCOMPANIED IMPROVISATION.... LISTEN/GIVE

Ⓓ bassoon/trombone duet:

CAN USE SOURCE MATERIAL FROM OBOE SOLO ... AND/OR SCALE STUFF .....

Ⓔ piano solo: oboe/tuba accompaniment (basson exit):

(use this synthetic Locrian material as you will rhythmically)

Ⓕ SILENCE... subito. ON CUE RECAP. Ⓐ SECTION

7 A | 3 C# | 6 D | 4 F# | 6 D | 2 F# | 5 G | 3 B | 4 C | 6 G# | 3 G | 7 D# | 5 G | 7 D# | 4 D | 8 A#

Ⓖ END WITH DOT-DOT-DASH TYPE PIZZICATO STUFF

ARHYMICALLY/SLOWLY DIMINISH DYNAMICS

ie. F → P → PP → PPP → O (subito)

fine

Eric Only Knew

This was realized similarly to "Choose Choice" or "But Then, The Kings." Dive in and go for it: maybe set up a color row? Stretch timbrally. As I've been saying, make it yours. Research Eric Dolphy; don't leave it merely to "Google." Read and listen to stuff about Eric Dolphy if you're not acquainted with him or his craft.

From Five on Down with Four

fine

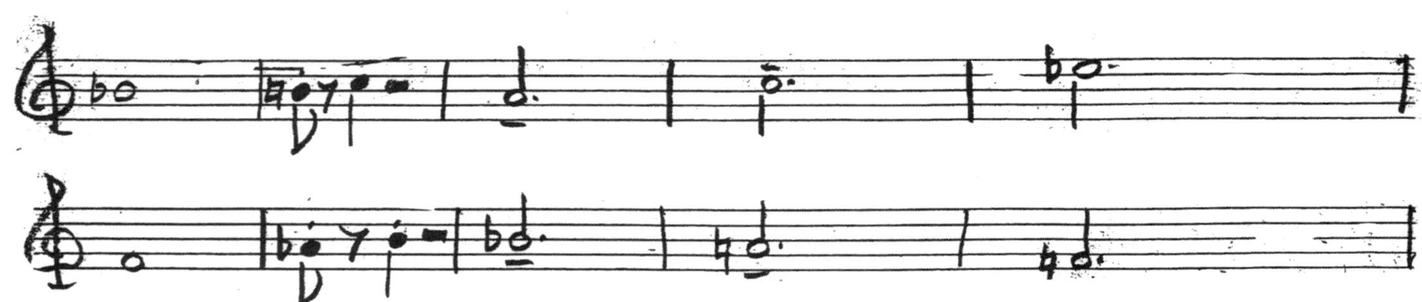

Glide I and Glide II

Heirloom

contrabass (cello)
Bm9
D+
DM7
E13
F#7#9
FM#11
E7#9
Am9
Dm9
Em9
E7#9
Am9
BbM#11
FM#11 (neopolitan)
FM9 (F Lydian Mode)
B
fine
D.C. al fine
1) cello and bassoon play head w/piano chording
2) then bassoon will take solo
3) " alto solo
4) " piano (accompanied by vibes)
SWITCH TO BASS
5) " bass and bassoon recap. head like beginning
cello

If You Ask Me

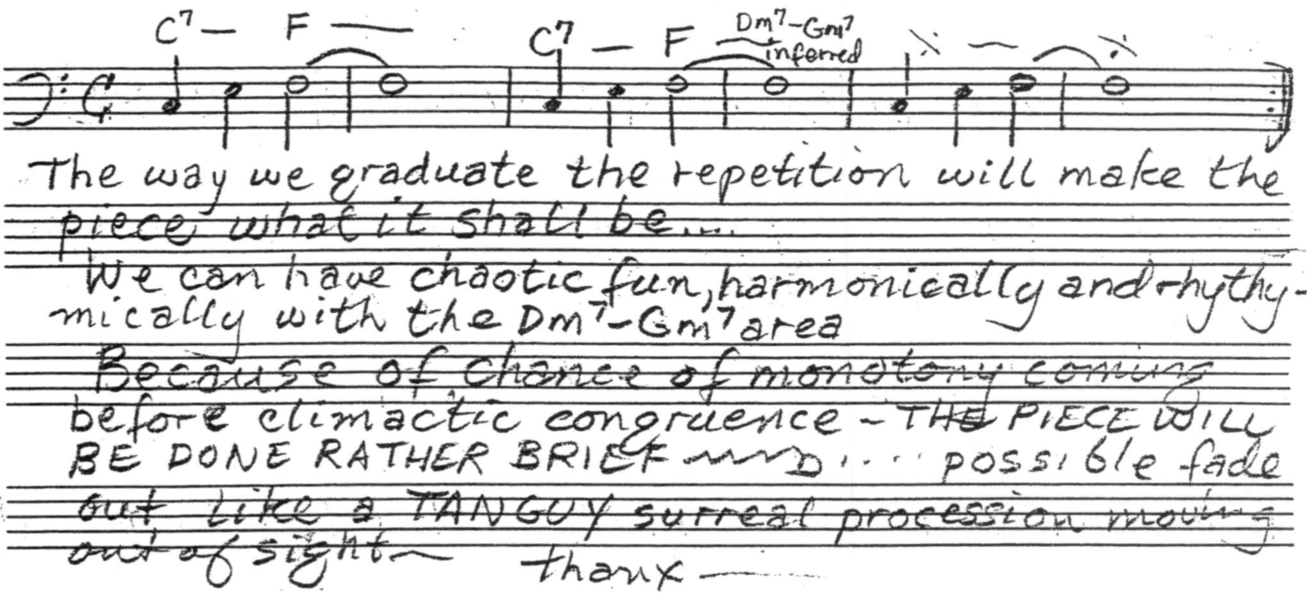
C7 — F —
C7 — F Dm7–Gm7 inferred
The way we graduate the repetition will make the piece what it shall be...
We can have chaotic fun, harmonically and rhythy-mically with the Dm7–Gm7 area
Because of chance of monotony coming before climactic congruence – THE PIECE WILL BE DONE RATHER BRIEF ... possible fade out like a TANGUY surreal procession moving out of sight
thanx —

Juxtaportation II

My Phononomaly Concept is an efflorescence of my Brief Reality Concept. I am interested in continuing to develop varying sound grounds—a kind of tonal fabric that consists of electronic and acoustic considerations used as a ground or canvas which can accommodate the collaborative endeavors of poetry, spoken word, dance, video, visual art forms, theatre, etc., along with their closest friend . . . SILENCE. The trick in developing "phononomalies" is to do as much as you can to make that which is recorded, that which is electronic, and that which is acoustic all sound like they are from the same source . . . LIFE FORCE.

"Juxtaportation" is to carry, send or be sent from one place to another for comparison and/or contrast. A prerecorded soundground was set by alto and bass clarinet and sound manipulation of assorted brass bells. This soundground was then improvised upon by nagasvaram, bass clarinet, grand piano, piano harp with mallet, Roland JD800 Synthesizer, Roland STP11 Drum Pad, voices, and bells. The complete Sound Window(s) work is an experimental sound study using voice, acoustical and electronic instrumentation for a quartet ensemble. Each of the four "windows" are peered through by its neighboring self/selves in a kaleidoscopic linear/dynamic way.

Kandinsky Lights to Dream On

Kandinsky Lights to Dream On (Continued)

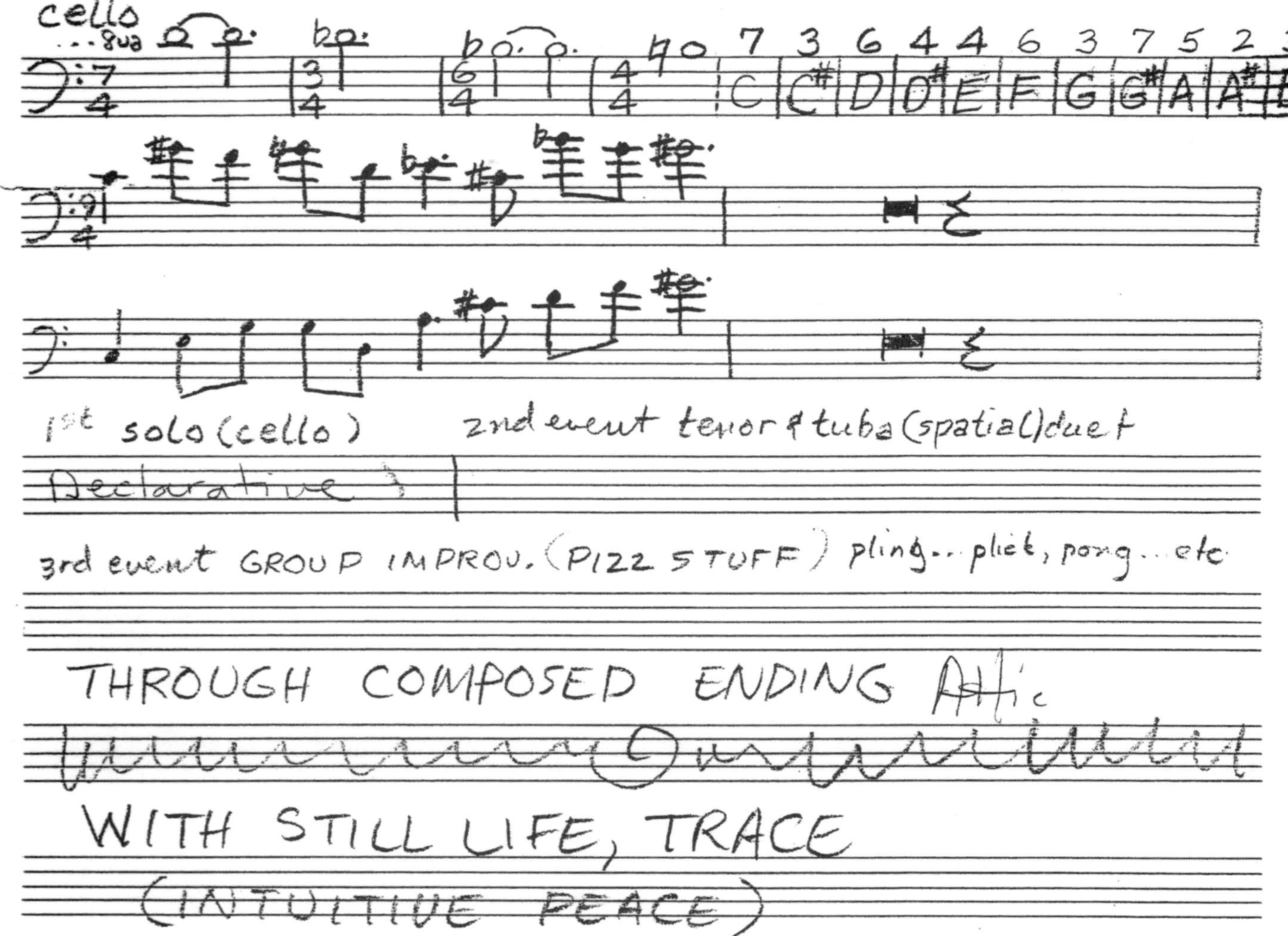

Kandinsky Lights to Dream On (Continued)

Kandinsky Lights to Dream On (Continued)

Kandinsky Lights to Dream On (Continued)

Kandinsky Lights to Dream On (Continued)

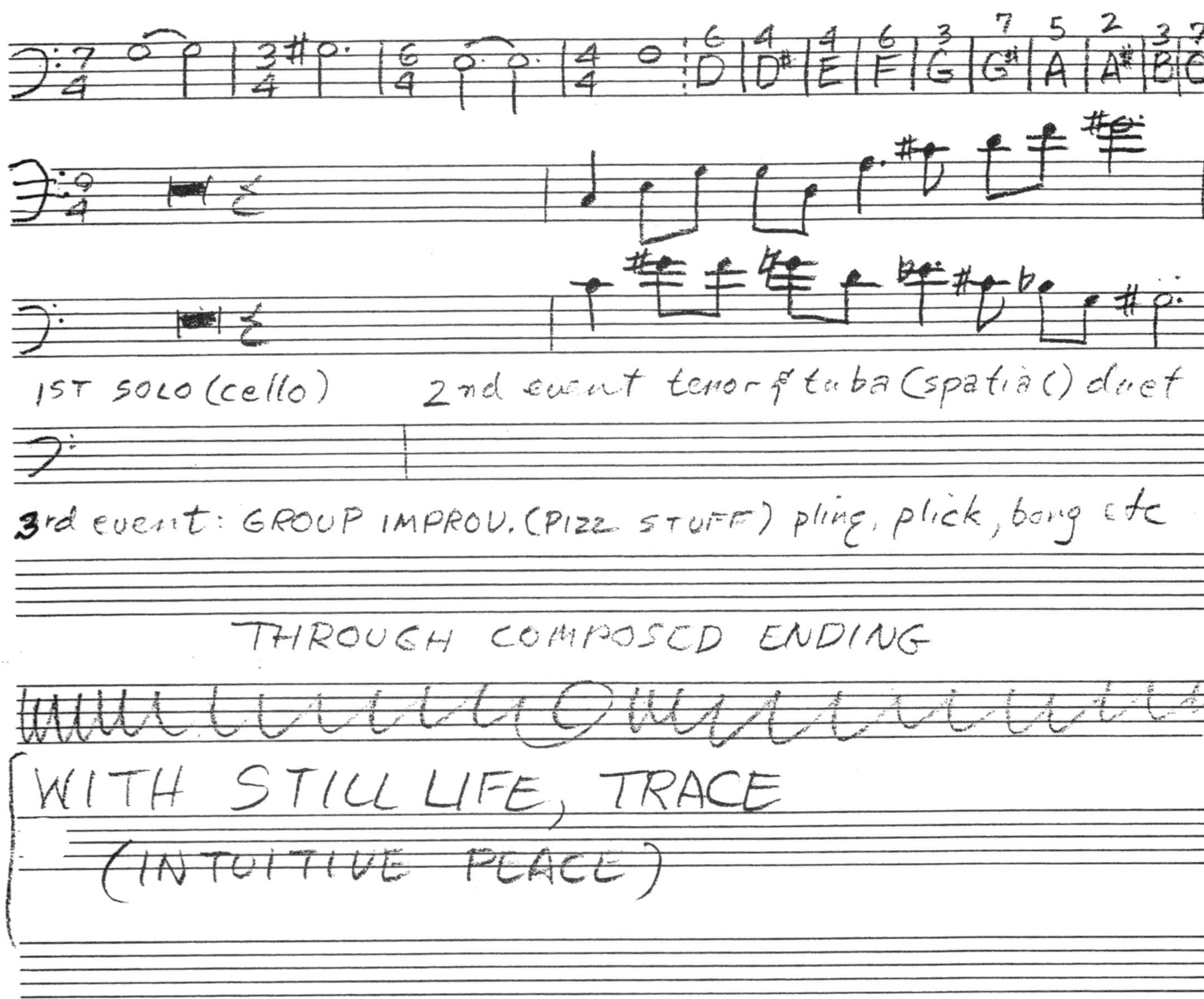

Kandinsky Static Antiphony

Carei F. Thomas
2001

Note: The standard notation that follows this page is an approximate representation of the matrix shown below.

The configuration - "≈ ≈" - I call "scrambles" and indicates for the instrumentalists to freely improvise with no thought to tonality but rather to emphasize timbral expression. Then, I add metric considerations. A number within a scramble designates its duration (i.e., ≈ ≈ with a 4 in it [≈ 4 ≈] equals four beats of free improvisation).

Oboe	≈4≈	C	≈3≈	G#	≈2≈	B	≈1≈	E	≈2≈	G	≈3≈	A#	≈4≈	D#
Alto Clarinet	A	≈3≈	F	≈2≈	Ab	≈1≈	Db	≈2≈	E	≈3≈	G	≈4≈	C	≈4≈
Bassoon	≈3≈	G#	≈2≈	B	≈1≈	E	≈2≈	G	≈3≈	A#	≈4≈	D#	≈4≈	C
Baritone Horn	G#	≈2≈	B	≈1≈	E	≈2≈	G	≈3≈	A#	≈4≈	D#	≈4≈	C	≈3≈
Marimba	≈2≈	B	≈1≈	E	≈2≈	G	≈3≈	A#	≈4≈	D#	≈4≈	C	≈3≈	G#
Piano	B	≈1≈	E	≈2≈	G	≈3≈	A#	≈4≈	D#	≈4≈	C	≈3≈	G#	≈2≈
Violin 1	≈1≈	E	≈2≈	G	≈3≈	A#	≈4≈	D#	≈4≈	C	≈3≈	G#	≈2≈	B
Violin 2	E	≈2≈	G	≈3≈	A#	≈4≈	D#	≈4≈	C	≈3≈	G#	≈2≈	B	≈1≈
Viola	≈2≈	G	≈3≈	A#	≈4≈	D#	≈4≈	C	≈3≈	G#	≈2≈	B	≈1≈	E
Violoncello	G	≈3≈	A#	≈4≈	D#	≈4≈	C	≈3≈	G#	≈2≈	B	≈1≈	E	≈2≈

Live Wire

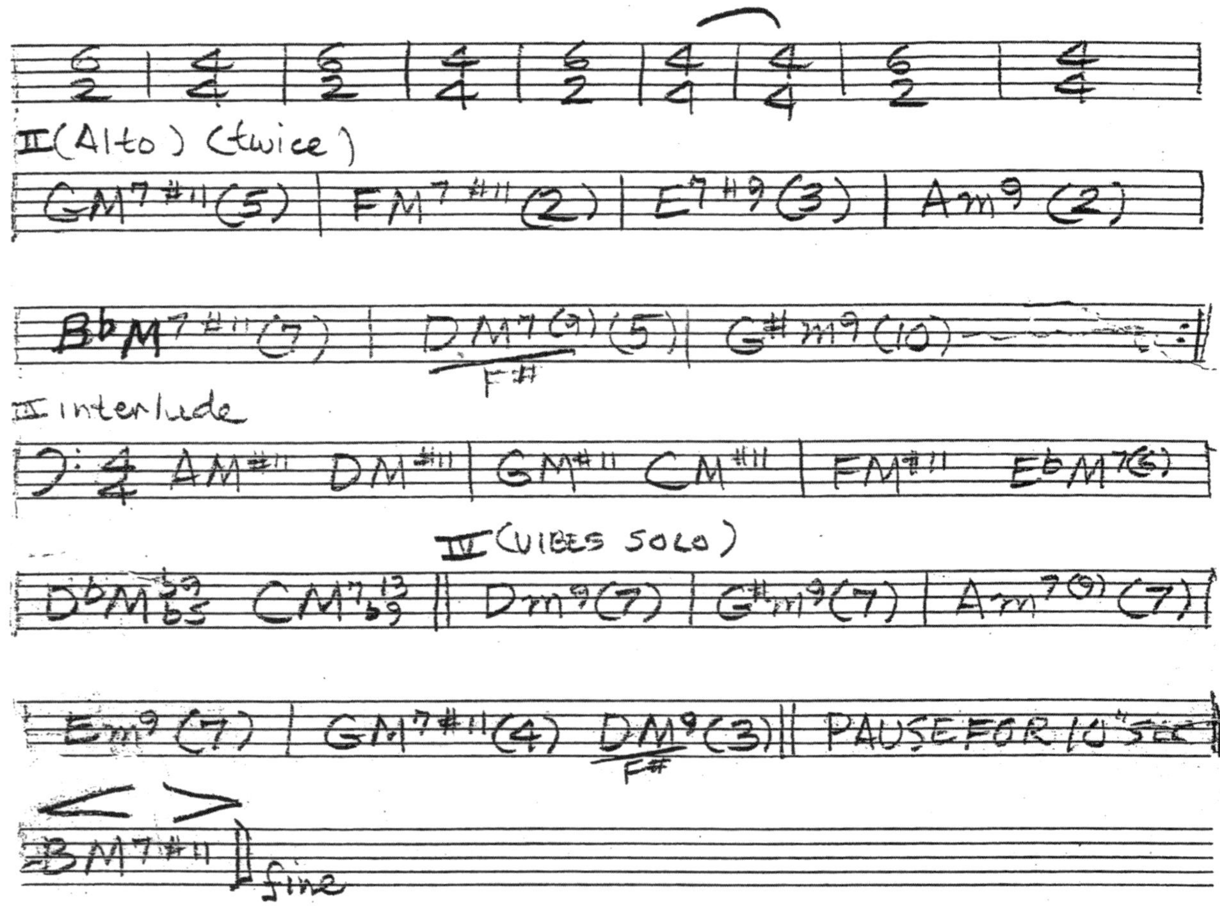
II (Alto) (twice)
GM7#11 (5) | FM7#11 (2) | E7#9 (3) | Am9 (2)
BbM7#11 (7) | DM7(9)/F# (5) | G#m9 (10)
III interlude
AM#11 DM#11 | GM#11 CM#11 | FM#11 EbM7(9)
DbM b9 b5 CM7 13 b9 || Dm9 (7) | G#m9 (7) | Am7(9) (7)
IV (VIBES SOLO)
Em9 (7) | GM7#11 (4) DM9/F# (3) || PAUSE FOR 10" SEC
BM7#11
fine

Magicmysticmaestromentor

Magicmysticmaestromentor

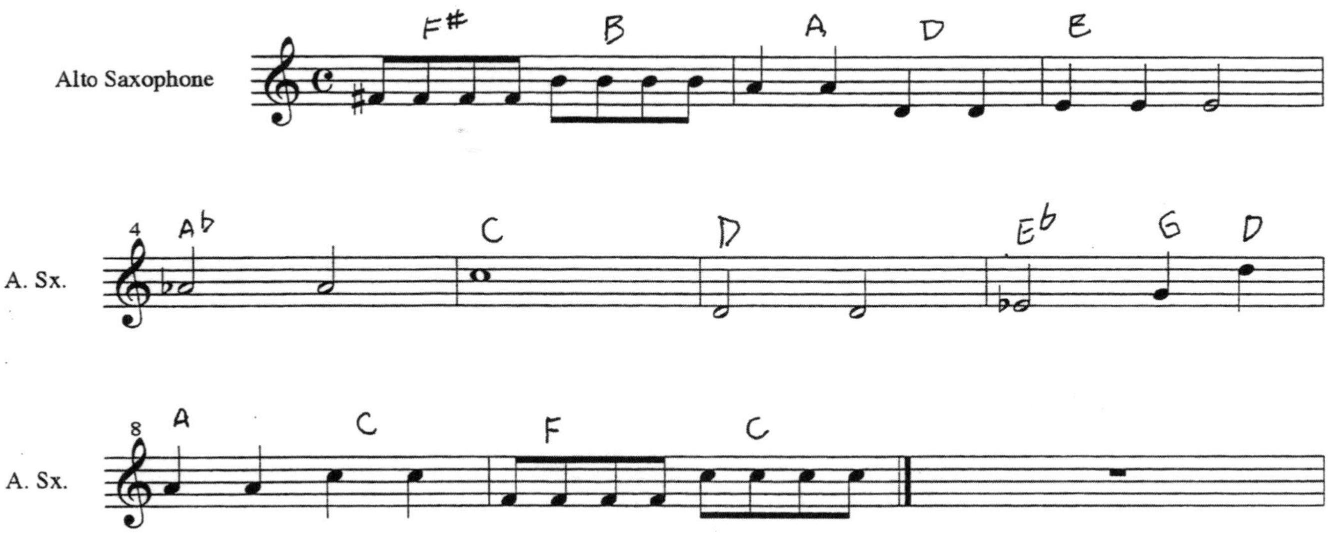

This row is used as an accompaniment. (36 beats = 9 measures of 4/4)
Notice the palindromic design which gives tension to the inner most measures.

(E^b instruments – transposed)

	2	3	4	5	6	5	4	3	2	
Gb	D	E	B	Eb	Ab	F	Bb	G	A	Db

To ground an already dense musical topography, I decided to unison-up the basic chordal/and bass ostinato areas: || 4/4 A – D | C – F | G | B | Eb | F | Gb – Bb – F | C- Eb | Ab – Eb || (See chords above measures.)

Morse Code

MORSE CODE set to Poem

```
W E          M U S T          C H A S E          T H E
.-- .        -- ..--... -     -.-..... .- ... .  - .... .

S H A D O W S                 F R O M            T H E
... .... .- -.. --- .-- ...   ..-. .-. --- --    - .... .

D A Y L I G H T;                              A N D        I N     T H I S
-.. .- -.-- .-... --. .... - -.-.-.           .- -. -..    .. -.   - .... .. ...

B R I L L I A N C E                     W E       W I L L
-....-. .. .-...-..... .- -. -.-..      .-- .     .-- .. .-...-..

D I S C E R N                T H E         V I T A L
-.. .. ... .-.-. .-. -.      - .... .      ...-.. - .- .-..

C O N N E C T I O N                   O F         N O W            A N D
-.-.---- -. -. . -.-.- .. --- -.      --- ..-.    -. --- .--       .- -. -..

I N F I N I T Y                       A L W H E R E
.. -. ..-... -. .. - -.--             .- .-...-- .... . .-. .
```

Nolemon|nomeloN

7 **G#**	6 **B**	3 **F**	5 **E**	4 **F#**	6 **B**	5 **G#**
6 **B**	3 **F**	5 **E**	4 **F#**	6 **B**	5 **G#**	7 **G#**
3 **F**	5 **E**	4 **F#**	6 **B**	5 **G#**	7 **G#**	6 **B**
5 **E**	4 **F#**	6 **B**	5 **G#**	7 **G#**	6 **B**	3 **F**
4 **F#**	6 **B**	5 **G#**	7 **G#**	6 **B**	3 **F**	5 **E**
6 **B**	5 **G#**	7 **G#**	6 **B**	3 **F**	5 **E**	4 **F#**
5 **G#**	7 **G#**	6 **B**	3 **F**	5 **E**	4 **F#**	6 **B**

"NOMELON" **(36 BEATS)**

5 **G#**	6 **B**	4 **F#**	5 **E**	3 **F**	6 **B**	7 **G#**
6 **B**	4 **F#**	5 **E**	3 **F**	6 **B**	7 **G#**	5 **G#**
4 **F#**	5 **E**	3 **F**	6 **B**	7 **G#**	5 **G#**	6 **B**
5 **E**	3 **F**	6 **B**	7 **G#**	5 **G#**	6 **B**	4 **F#**
3 **F**	6 **B**	7 **G#**	5 **G#**	6 **B**	4 **F#**	5 **E**
6 **B**	7 **G#**	5 **G#**	6 **B**	4 **F#**	5 **E**	3 **F**
7 **G#**	5 **G#**	6 **B**	4 **F#**	5 **E**	3 **F**	6 **B**

Paradigm I

(concert)								
B♭ trumpet TRANSPOSED →	7 C# (E♭)	3 C (D)	6 F (G)	4 G (A)	4 B♭ (C)	6 E (G♭)	3 G# (B♭)	7 D# (F)
E♭ alto sax TRANSPOSED →	3 C (A)	6 F (D)	4 G (E)	4 B♭ (G)	6 E (D♭)	3 G# (F)	7 D# (C)	7 C# (B♭)
B♭ tenor sax TRANSPOSED →	6 F (G)	4 G (A)	4 B♭ (C)	6 E (G♭)	3 G# (B♭)	7 D# (F)	7 C# (E♭)	3 C (D)
cello	4 G	4 B♭	6 E	3 G#	7 D#	7 C#	3 C	6 F
vibes	4 B♭	6 E	3 G#	7 D#	7 C#	3 C	6 F	4 G
guitar	6 E	3 G#	7 D#	7 C#	3 C	6 F	4 G	4 B♭
piano	3 G#	7 D#	7 C#	3 C	6 F	4 G	4 B♭	6 E
	7 D#	7 C#	3 C	6 F	4 G	4 B♭	6 E	3 G#

Period

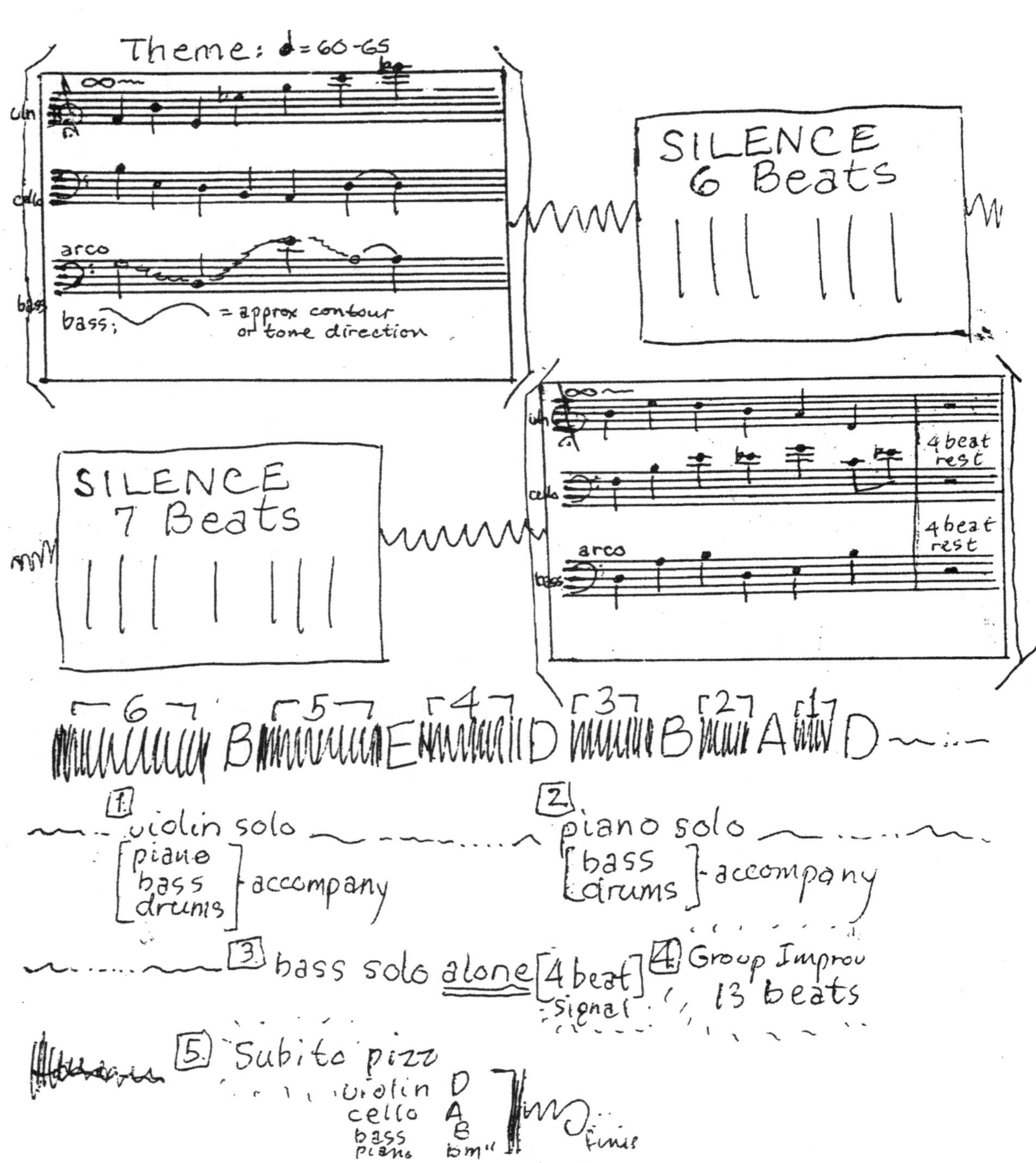
Theme: 𝅗𝅥 = 60-65
vln
cello
arco
bass
bass: = approx contour or tone direction
SILENCE
6 Beats
SILENCE
7 Beats
4 beat rest
4 beat rest
arco
6 B 5 E 4 D 3 B 2 A 1 D
1. violin solo
piano
bass
drums
accompany
2. piano solo
bass
drums
accompany
3. bass solo alone
4 beat signal
4. Group Improv
13 beats
5. Subito pizz
violin D
cello A
bass E
piano
finis

Poemmetry

"Poemmetry" is a spatial-kinetic-music-word concept. It is using words, phrases and onomatopoetic expressions in conjunction with larger developed works of poetry. The participants can take on varying formations (dyads, triads, etc.). Poemmetry utilizes poetry and the audience in making the compositional fabric work. This is similar to the way fragments of written musical material hold "brief realities" together (like a kind of skin or connective tissue).

> "Brief Realities" are an efflorescence of controlled improvisational concepts. They are ever-changing series of purely invented music often spiced with cells or fragments of written material acting like connective tissue. I feel this improvisational concept gives performaers a structure that defines and focuses content while offering a broad choice of source material harmonically, temporally, dynamically and culturally. Within this tonal order, invention/improvisation ignites the developmental process that creates the true composition (and allows it to remain everychangingly fresh).

Some examples of "poemmetry" phrases that could be used with audience participation are the following:

MAKIN' SURE
AND THEN WHAT?
THAT'LL BE FIVE MORE SENSE
WHO TOOK THE ONIONS?
WHAT'S BURNIN'?
NO PROBLEM
WHAT?
WE THOUGHT IT WAS CANDY
NOT ENOUGH HAMBURGER
IN THE NEAR FUTURE
THE FACTS ALONE HAVE NO SALT
CHICKEN KIDNEYS?
THERE BETTER BE CHILDREN
DID YOU SMELL THAT?
LET'S CALL THIS
AMERICAN, AS IT SHOULD BE
THE BALLOON'S GOING UP
A LITTLE TO THE RIGHT
A LITTLE TO THE LEFT
I HOLD YOU RESPONSIBLE
THE SIZZLE NOT THE STEAK
VEGETABLE FOOD IS GOOD
I BET YOU KNOW WHAT I MEAN
PEOPLE PUZZLE PROPOSITION
MUDDY WATERS SHO WAS RIGHT
THAT'S STILL NO REASON TO DIE

Side Show Color Row

Cell 1:

3			2		4	2		5		2	2
D	**A**	**G#**	**D**	**G**	**A**	**F#**	**E**	**C**	**B**	**F**	**G#**
2		4		2	2	2			5	3	
B	**F#**	**G#**	**E**	**A**	**D**	**D#**	**G**	**C**	**C#**	**A#**	**F**
	2		2		5	3			4	3	
A	**E**	**G**	**B**	**C#**	**G#**	**C**	**F#**	**E**	**F**	**A#**	**D**

Cell 2:

	3	5			2	2	2		4		2
F	**A#**	**C#**	**C**	**G**	**D#**	**D**	**A**	**E**	**G#**	**F#**	**B**
	3	4			3	5		2		2	
D	**A#**	**F**	**E**	**F#**	**C**	**G#**	**C#**	**B**	**G**	**E**	**A**
2	2		5		2	4		2			3
G#	**F**	**B**	**C**	**E**	**F#**	**A**	**G**	**D**	**C#**	**A#**	**D#**

Sky Extensions

E^b

(70 beats)

Locale I.

C – Bb – Ab – Eb – F – [7 Dbm9] – [5 AM#11] – B – A – [4 Abm9] – D

G – E – C – [5 Dm11] – A – Gb – D – B – Eb – Ab – Db – Bb – A – D

(7 EM9(6)) (7 Bm+7(b9))

G – C – F – Bb – Eb – Ab Db – Gb – B – E – Db – Bb – B

(6 C°+7) (5 Dbm9)

Locale II.

(70 beats)

[7 Fm11] – Eb – F – [4 Dbm9] – B – A – D – [2 AM#11] – [2 Bbm11] – [1 Am7]

[4 Abm9] – Gb – D – B – [5 Dm11] – Eb – Ab – Db – [4 EM9(6)] – Bb – A – D – G

C – F – [7 C°+7] – Eb – Ab – Db – Gb – B – E – Db – Bb – B

Locale III.

(70 beats)

C – [5 Fm11] – [3 Dbm9] – Gb – B – A – D – G

[3 Abm9] – E – C – [2 Abm9] – [5 Bm11] – [7 Dm11]

A – Gb – D – [5 Bm+7(b9)] – B – Eb – Ab – Db – Gb – B

E – Db – Bb – B

Enough said!!!

Stellium 6

STELLIUM 6

USE JUPITER AND PLUTO WISELY

EXPANSION

MERCURY (A)	VENUS (B)	MARS (D)	JUPITER (E)
C#7#9b13	D#7#9b13	F#7#9b13	D# ∞ F#

ESTRUCTION

SATURN (F)	URANUS (G)	PLUTO (A#)
A7#9b13	B7#9b13	clusters A# D# D♮

Color spiral formation:

‖: A | B | D | E | F | G | A# :‖ (3 2 4 2 3 2) OR RETROGRADE (Keep going for a while (smile)

Solo I: STEVE → Solo II CAREI ...

→ PIZZICATO splinter EXCHANGE → | A | B | D | E | F | G | A# (3 2 4 2 3 2)

GO TO CHIRON FREELY

→ WELCOME TO FEBRUARY

Thanx
NAM-MYOHO-RENGE-KYO
– Carei – 1-21-90

Talegating

The Reconstruction of Light
(Performance Design)

~ The Reconstruction of Light ~

I. Photochromokinesis

piccolo: $\overset{4}{B}b - \overset{2}{G} - Eb - C - \overset{3}{A} - \overset{2}{F} - D - Gb - \overset{3}{B} - \overset{4}{E} - \overset{2}{D}b$

hsiao: $\overset{2}{B}b - G - Eb - \overset{3}{C} - \overset{2}{A} - F - D - \overset{3}{G}b - \overset{4}{B} - \overset{2}{E} - \overset{4}{D}b$

violin: $Bb - G - \overset{3}{E}b - \overset{2}{C} - A - F - \overset{3}{D} - \overset{4}{G}b - \overset{2}{B} - \overset{4}{E} - \overset{2}{D}b$

cello: $Bb - \overset{3}{G} - \overset{2}{E}b - C - A - \overset{3}{F} - \overset{4}{D} - \overset{2}{G}b - \overset{4}{B} - \overset{2}{E} - Db$

piano: $\overset{3}{B}b - \overset{2}{G} - Eb - C - \overset{3}{A} - \overset{4}{F} - \overset{2}{D} - \overset{4}{G}b - \overset{2}{B} - E - Db$

harp: $\overset{2}{B}b - G - Eb - \overset{3}{C} - \overset{4}{A} - \overset{2}{F} - \overset{4}{D} - \overset{2}{G}b - B - E - \overset{3}{D}b$

BRIEF REALITY I: HARP SOLO

II. Juxtaportation

.... enter John M. reciting "The Reconstruction of Light"

	7	3	6	4	6	2	5	3	4	6	3	7	5	7	4	8
clarinet ~	G#	B	E	F	C#	E	A	A#	B	A#	F	D	F#	F	C	A
violin ~	D	D	G#	B	G	G	C#	F#	G	D	G#	G#	G	A	D#	D#
French Horn ~	A	C#	D	F#	D	F#	G	B	C	G#	G	D#	G	D#	D	A#
cello —	B	A#	A	A#	G	F#	C	B	C	C#	G	G#	B	A#	B	C
piano	CHORDAL PROGRESSION FROM "DREAM"...															
harp	"LIGHT" ARABESQUES ~~~→															
percussion (John M.)	~~~→															

BRIEF REALITY II: FRENCH HORN SOLO

¿ $A - \overset{3}{F} - \overset{2}{G} - \overset{4}{D} - Gb - B - Ab - \overset{2}{D}b - \overset{2}{B}b - \overset{5}{E} - \overset{2}{C}$ (or) STATIC ANTIPHONAL DESIGN (BRIEF)

III. Phononomaly ¿enter Carei T. reciting "New Colors Coming"

(Helix-like piece) ~~→ EVERYONE ~~→ End

Try All and Heir

I began doing Brief Realities with the Improvisational Piano Trio: Triade (1986). We did them at the beginning of our performances as a way to warm up, acknowledge, and communicate with that spirit energy that connects us to each other, the space, and the audience. From time to time, I use fragma of writeen material as connective tissue. Within this tonal order, invention/improvisation ignites the developmental process that creates the true composition (and allows it to remain everchangingly fresh). Not so quiet as its kept, this is what I'm after throughout this performance for us not to be shackled by a lot of manuscript.

EVENT I	EVENT II	EVENT III	EVENT IV	EVENT V	EVENT VI
Oboe	Oboe	Oboe	Oboe	Oboe	Piccolo
	Alto Clarinet	Alto Clarinet	Alto Clarinet	Alto Clarinet	
		Bassoon	Bassoon	Bassoon	
			Baritone H	Baritone H	
				Marimba	
				Piano	
			Violin	Violin	
		Violin	Violin	Violin	
	Viola	Viola	Viola	Viola	
Cello	Cello	Cello	Cello	Cello	Tuba

Tryptycht

© 1997 Carei F. Thomas

This is an example of the aforementioned color row for spiral building concept.

Violin:

		3	2			4	2	2		5	3
E	F	C#	C	G	G#	A#	B	A	D#	F#	D

Viola:

	3	2			4	2	2		5	3	
F	C#	C	G	C	A#	B	A	D#	F#	D	E

Bassoon:

2	2			4	2	2		5	3		
C#	C	G	G#	A#	B	A	D	F#	D	E	F

B♭ Clarinet:

3	2			4	2	2		5	3		
E♭	D	A	B♭	C	D♭	B	F	A♭	E	G♭	G

JD800:

2			4	2	2		5	3			3
C	G	G#	A#	B	A	D#	F#	D	E	F	C#

Drums: Improvise (fill)

Tryptychyt—Part II:

Starts with Roland JD800 (2-way slide patch on G—a perfect fifth down.
Other instruments are directed to do similar contouring—spontaneous invention.

With Joan Miró in Mind, Paul and Carla, Too

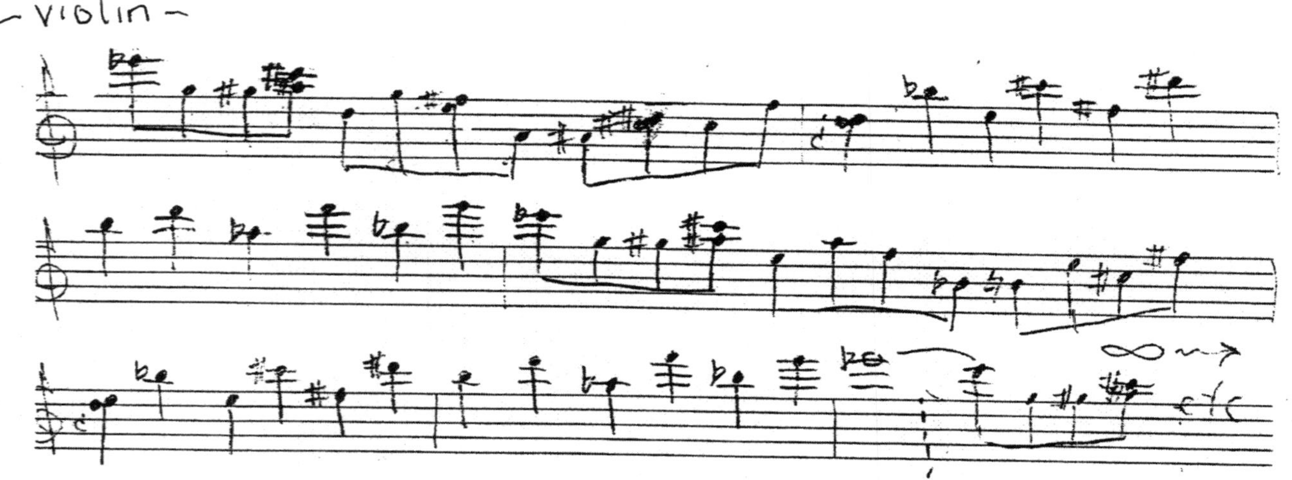

With Joan Miró in Mind, Paul and Carla, Too (Continued)

With Joan Miró in Mind, Paul and Carla, Too (Continued)

When I Look Back

INDEX BY CONCEPT